MILITIA LISTS and MUSTERS
1757 - 1876

A Directory of holdings in the British Isles

Jeremy Gibson and Mervyn Medlycott

Federation of Family History Societies

Published by the
Federation of Family History Societies,
c/o Benson Room, Birmingham and Midland Institute,
Margaret Street, Birmingham B3 3BS, England.

ISBN 1 872094 02 3

Cover and title page graphics by Linda Haywood.
Cover illustration: detail from an engraving of Supplementary Infantry, the New Levies of 1796.

Typeset from computer disks prepared by Jeremy Gibson and printed by Parchment (Oxford) Limited.

Acres: O Sir Lucius! I have had ancestors too! Every man of 'em colonel or captain in the militia!

Richard Brinsley Sheridan: *The Rivals*, Act III, Scene 4.

ACKNOWLEDGMENTS

Work on compiling this Guide started some years ago, and archivists have as always been generous with time and effort in replying to questionnaires from both of us, and subsequent enquiries. We hope that the discovery of hitherto unsuspected records will be at least a partial return for all their help.

We should like thank too Dr Ian Beckett, the acknowledged authority on British auxiliary forces; Alan Dell, co-author of the companion Guide to *Tudor and Stuart Muster Rolls*; and Tom Stoate, whose publications of transcripts of West Country records are an example to the rest; for sharing their knowledge and experience. With particular areas, we are grateful for aid from Cliff Webb (Surrey), Jean Cole (Wiltshire), Glyn Parry (N.L.W.) and Sheila and John Rowlands (Wales).

J.S.W.G. and M.T.M.

PREFACE

As with all Guides in this series, our primary object is to provide precise information on the survival and location of comprehensive or extensive lists of personal names which may be of use in family historical research. Thus administrative records, or lists with severely restricted numbers of names, such as those listing officers only, are omitted. There is no claim to exhaustive or authoritative coverage of the whole field of records engendered by the part-time forces known as the Militia.

The majority of sixteenth and seventeenth century records are in the Public Record Office, Chancery Lane, London, or the Scottish Record Office. These are described in the companion Guide to *Tudor and Stuart Muster Rolls*.

The later records, listed in this Guide, are of the reconstituted Militia from 1757 on, and various others engendered by the Napoleonic Wars between 1797 and 1815. As described by Sir Mervyn Medlycott, parishes were liable to provide a small number of men for training, but these were initially chosen from most able-bodied men. Thus lists of all those eligible had to be drawn up, from which the ballot was made, and where these survive (between 1757 and 1831), they provide a quasi census. We have called these *Militia Ballot Lists*. The 'Defence Lists', *Posse Comitatus* (1798) and *Levee en Masse* (1803-4), also provide wide census-type information. It is these population lists which must be of greatest interest to family and local historians, and Sir Mervyn has made an exhaustive survey of such records in local authority record offices in England and Wales. As the Militia and other measures were the responsibility of the Lord Lieutenants of individual counties, some of their records may still be in private collections. No attempt has been made to survey these, but information would be welcome.

Much more frequently surviving are the *Muster Rolls* or *Enrolment Books* of those few who were actually chosen in the ballot, or their paid substitutes. Particularly where these show parish of origin they can still be of restricted use to family and local historians. They too are mostly in local authority record offices, who have provided the information included here. Where we have been able to discover them, holdings in Ireland, the Channel Isles and the Isle of Man are also included.

In Scotland there are many pre-Union (1707) *Muster Rolls* amongst individual family collections now in the Scottish Record Office, listed in *Tudor and Stuart Muster Rolls*. Other relevant eighteenth century records, particularly around 1745-6, are included here. The Militia in Scotland was only re-established in 1793, but from the later eighteenth century and during the Napoleonic wars and thereafter the private collections again include muster rolls and occasionally the census-type records. The listing given is based on a search by myself of the card index catalogue at the Scottish Record Office, but there was no opportunity to examine individual records. In some cases collections may include unidentified lists and, again, further information will be welcomed. It is probable, too, that private Scottish muniments might provide many more lists of interest.

Muster rolls of regiments of Militia, 1780-1876; Supplementary Militia, 1798-1816; and Local Militia, 1808-16 are in Class WO.13 at the Public Record Office, Kew, and specific references are shown under counties *etc*. These lists, though voluminous, are of little practical use, as they do not normally indicate any places of origin (but see Bucks., 1831). However, they may assist if an individual is

3

already identified as serving in a regiment, or, of course, if research of a more general nature on the militia is required.

Muster rolls of other bodies in WO.13 (not listed in this Guide) include those for Fencibles: Cavalry [3726-85], Provisional Cavalry [3786-91] and Infantry [3792-3967]; Yeomanry: Cavalry [3968-4058] and Ireland [4059-4159]; and Volunteers (1797-1814) [4160-4621]; (1873-78) [4622-75]. The lists of 1797-1814 Volunteers are the most promising. Within each county many larger places are individually named, presumably as the centres of local organisation. Unfortunately as there are approaching five hundred references, space and time preclude their inclusion here. Individual county lists could easily be abstracted for publication in family history magazines.

By the later nineteenth century there are plenty of other sources of names for family historians, so we have in general excluded any records of the militia or other voluntary bodies after the 1870's, whether held centrally or locally.

Jeremy Gibson

THE MILITIA BALLOT LISTS, 1757-1831, AND 'DEFENCE' LISTS, 1798-1804

(Mostly based, by kind permission, on the article 'Some Georgian "Censuses"', *The Genealogists' Magazine*, **23**, 2 (June 1989))

Whilst the nineteenth century census records from 1841 on are a staple diet for family and local historians, other earlier census-type sources have to date received very little attention. These are the Militia Ballot Lists, 1757-1831, and the 'defence lists', 1798 and 1803-4.

Militia Ballot Lists, 1757-1831

In the 1757 Militia Act (30 Geo. II c25) Parliament ordered that militia regiments be re-established, after a period of dormancy, in counties of England and Wales. It was realised from the start that insufficient volunteers could be induced to come forward to serve in the ranks. An alternative was therefore introduced, a form of conscription in which parishes made lists of adult males, and then ballots were held to choose some of them for compulsory service. If the chosen men were not willing to serve in person then they were required to find other men to serve in their stead as substitutes.

The limited lists of men chosen in the ballots – known as principals or 'drawn men' – and substitutes, are in this Guide called *Militia Muster Rolls* or *Enrolment Lists*. These are not what are known as *Militia Lists* (in this Guide called *Militia Ballot Lists*), which were the much more impressive documents containing the names of all the men liable to the ballot. Although in a few counties militia ballot lists were not compiled, as sufficient volunteers came forward to fill the militia quotas, and other counties took some years after 1757 to establish their regiments, the majority of counties in England and Wales by the early 1760's were staging annual ballots requiring yearly lists of names to be compiled.

Militia recruitment was not organised through Quarter Sessions but by a separate organisation, the County Lieutenancy, under the control of the Privy Council, led by the Lord Lieutenant through Deputy Lieutenants and magistrates down to parish constables and tithingmen. Parishes were grouped together into balloting districts, being hundreds, wapentakes or newly-created administrative areas known as sub-divisions, there being one for each company in the militia regiments.

Under the 1757 Act the parish constables were ordered annually to record the names of all men aged 18 to 50, excluding only those who were peers, clergy, teachers, apprentices and 'peace officers'. However in the 1758 Act (31 Geo II c26) and therafter until 1831, Parliament directed that no names be excluded, although the upper age limit was lowered to 45 from 1762.

The militia ballot lists should therefore be in theory complete annual censuses of all men aged 18 to 50, from 1758 to 1762, and aged 18 to 45, from 1762 to 1831. As explained below, it is unlikely that all were complete. There are good collections for six counties and one city: Cumberland, Dorset, Hertfordshire, Kent, Lincolnshire, Northamptonshire and Bristol; significant holdings in fifteen other counties, and various parishes in eighteen more. Many of these have lain unnoticed amongst records of serving militiamen in county lieutenancy papers in provincial record offices.

The value of militia lists is not only that survivals are more widespread than had been thought, and that they are good census substitutes recording people across the whole social spectrum, but in the fascinating details on each man that they can give. Parliament laid down in the Militia Acts the minimum information that must be provided on each man, which can be summarised as follows:

1757-1758: Names and infirmities.
1758-1802: Names, occupations and infirmities.
1802-1806: Names, descriptions, infirmities, numbers of children aged over and under 14 (and in household forms, ages).
1806-1831: Names, descriptions, ages, infirmities, and numbers of children aged over and under 14.

Additionally, information was to be given on those men who had already served a term in the militia and details on units of men serving in the Volunteer Infantry and Yeomanry.

Some parish constables chose to provide still more information, particularly in the 1757 to 1802 period. They needed to identify categories of men who were eligible for exemption from the ballots, and the details they added helped them to do this. The numbers of children men had aged under 10 are quite frequently given in the Hertfordshire lists from the 1760's, and in those for Northamptonshire for the 1770's. The occasional parish before 1802 even gives ages. The most important ones to do so were Greenwich and the two parishes in Deptford, Kent, for 1,253 men in 1757.

One county lieutenancy, that of Dorset in the 1790's, seems to have made its own rules as to what was to be recorded, far beyond what Parliament decreed. They give almost consistently throughout the four-fifths of the county that has militia lists surviving between 1796 and 1799, names, occupations, infirmities, heights in feet and inches, marital status, numbers of children aged under 10, and which were 'young men' in the age group.

The 1802 Militia Act (42 Geo. III c90) laid down that many more details were to be recorded for all men on printed household and parish forms. Up to 1801 it seems likely that the constables compiled the lists personally by visiting each house. The 1802 Act ordered that printed household (schedule A) forms were to be distributed to each householder, who then filled them in and passed them back to the constables. The information was then transferred onto parish (schedule B) lists. Under the 1802 Act the household forms required ages to be recorded but rather oddly the parish lists did not. The 1806 Militia Act (46 Geo. III c91) ordered ages to be given in the parish lists.

Regrettably few of the schedule A household forms survive, apart from those of 1828 for Westminster. This, though, is the largest single collection of militia lists located, complete for the entire City of Westminster, around 30,000 names, and all of them on schedule A household forms, giving also householders' names.

In the column marked 'description', Parliament specified that this was to indicate a man's position in the household, such as inmate, lodger or servant. However, fortunately, most people wrote down occupations instead. As exemption from the militia ballot was offered for those who 'laboured under infirmities', an entertaining and exaggerated variety of these may be specified.

How census-like or complete are the militia ballot lists? Though the Militia Acts from 1758 decreed that the lists must give all men, it is clear that this did not always happen. There were certain categories of men eligible for exemption from the ballots. It would seem understandable that some parish constables chose to omit those names, despite official instructions not to do so. There may also have been some evasion and bribery of constables.

In the 1802 Act a procedure of producing amended lists was instituted. The schedule A household forms included even the names of householders who were men over 45, and women. These were first of all to be omitted from the schedule B parish lists – although in the Ely and South Witchford Hundreds of Cambridgeshire lists of c.1802-9 it has been noticed that sometimes this did not happen. The parish constables were then instructed to strike out the names of those eligible for exemption from the ballot and to prepare new lists omitting them. Further names were struck out and amended lists made after appeals had been heard by the magistrates. The final lists were then entered in what we call *Militia 'Liable' Books*. In a few counties have been found separate books with the names of those exempted from the ballots – *Militia 'Exempt' Books*.

One would expect that only the final amended lists would be preserved with earlier versions being discarded, but this is not always so, not even for those filed in county lieutenancy papers. It may be that the earlier unamended versions were sometimes retained as a record of men granted exemptions, to have available for reference when new lists were made the following year. The 1803 lists for Lincoln and Sleaford Sub-divisions survive in two versions, original and amended, in the Kesteven lieutenancy records.

A fair rule of thumb can be applied for those concerned to know how complete is each list. If it contains few or no names struck out it must be that this is near to the final amended version. If, however (and this appears to be generally the case with most eighteenth century lists) there are large numbers of names struck out, then it must be an early version and nearest, if the deleted names are included, to recording all men in the age group.

To aid such an assessment one needs to know the categories of men eligible for exemption from the ballot, which may be summarised as follows:

1. Occupations: clergy, teachers, medical men, apprentices, university members and peers.
2. Officials: M.P.s, judges, magistrates, constables and 'other peace officers'.
3. Serving soldiers and sailors, former militiamen, and (during the Napoleonic Wars) men serving in the volunteers and yeomanry.
4. Men under a certain height, mostly 5 feet 4 inches.
5. Men 'labouring under infirmities'.
6. Men with more than a certain number of children 'born in wedlock', mostly three or four children aged under 10 before 1802, and those with any children under 14 thereafter.

Ballots were not only held for recruitment of men into the 'regular' militias, but also for the Supplementary Militias, 1796-1816, Army of Reserve, 1803-4, and Local Militias, 1808-13. Separate militia ballot lists have been found in various counties for these, particularly for the Army of Reserve in Cambridgeshire, Kent, Sussex, and Bristol. They all seem to contain much the same details on men as the 'regular' Militia ballot lists, and were for the same age groups, with the exception of the Local Militia lists, confined to men aged 18 to 30.

Enforced conscription by use of the militia ballot was almost universally hated by the civilian population, its introduction in 1757 being the cause of widespread rioting, and again in 1796 when the supplementary militia ballot was applied.

Opposition steadily grew during the 1820's and this led to the ballot being suspended in 1829. The government tried to reintroduce it in 1831 at the time of the Reform Bill riots when the militias were re-embodied. The 1831 lists were compiled, even ballot cards made ready, but this led to such an outcry that the ballot was not held and no further lists were made. Thereafter the Militias raised recruits from volunteers only.

'Defence Lists', 1798 and 1803-4

This is an apt collective name for the *Posse Comitatus* lists of 1798 made under the Defence of the Realm Act (38 Geo. III c27) and the *Levee en Masse* lists of 1803-4 under the 1st and 2nd Defence Acts (43 Geo. III c55 and c96). The 'Defence Lists' are so similar in appearance to the militia ballot lists that they have often been confused with them.

The 'Defence Lists' were not compiled for use in any ballot, and none of the people given in them were intended to be recruited into the militias. Their compilation was to organise reserves of men who were not already serving in a military capacity for the defence of Britain against French invasion. These men were needed to evacuate the civil population, remove cattle and crops from the path of the invader, gather up arms and equipment in private hands, and transport and supply food to the defending forces. They were also to be grouped into *posses* of pioneers and special constables to harry the enemy and quell internal insurrection. Of course we all know that, as in 1940, the invasion never happened, but the preparations were nevertheless urgent and in most places meticulously organised.

For the *Posse Comitatus* lists of 1798 and the *Levee en Masse* under the 1st Defence Act of June 1803, parish constables were ordered to record the names and occupations of all able-bodied men not already employed in a military capacity aged between 15 and 60, together with other schedules listing millers, bakers, and waggon and barge owners.

The *Levee en Masse* under the 2nd Defence Act of July 1803 was much more comprehensive, amounting to a census of the entire population by name if all the many schedules were completed. These schedules come into the following categories:

1. All men aged 17 to 55, giving names, occupations and infirmities, arranged in four categories according to age group, marital status, and numbers of children aged under 10. Also occasionally stated are the men's exact ages.
2. All householders, giving names, sometimes occupations and ages, and whether Quakers or aliens, with numbers of males and females in each household.
3. Non-combatants who would need to be evacuated, women, children, the old and infirm, being 'incapable of removing themselves', giving names, sometimes also occupations and ages.
4. Some of the men aged 17-55 formed into *posses* of pioneers and special constables.
5. Miscellaneous categories including lists of millers, bakers, waggon and barge owners, guides, stockmen, waggoners and those holding weapons. Also schedules of numbers of farm animals and amounts of corn and fodder to be removed.

The July 1803 *Levee en Masse* lists were so complex that for some places (such as Barnstaple in Devon and Rowbarrow Hundred in Dorset) digests were made

8

from all the schedules which were censuses of the entire population. Complete censuses could also be produced out of a combination of lists 1 and 3, and for householders and population in list 2.

Fortunately the *Posse Comitatus* lists for the whole of Buckinghamshire (published) and most of Northumberland survive in county lieutenancy records. There are however relatively few for other counties, just clusters of parishes here or there.

Most of the detailed *Levee en Masse* lists were retained by their compilers, officials known as captains of hundreds and boroughs. Only statistical summaries were forwarded to the county lieutenancies and the Privy Council. In consequence few lists survive, and most of them are for the first category, the men aged 17-55, such as for the Rape of Pevensey, Sussex, with 6,419 men recorded in 51 parishes (published); the Hundreds of Barford, Stodden and Willey in Bedfordshire; and Staincliffe with Ewcross Wapentake in the West Riding of Yorkshire. The most comprehensive and census-like survivals mostly seem to be in borough collections, such as Folkestone in Kent, Poole in Dorset, and Exeter. It is to be hoped that the publication of this Guide will bring more to light, particularly from private archives, once they have become better known.

Other forces

Those men who enlisted in the Militias served for three years in the period 1757-86 and five years thereafter. In peacetime they lived at home but spent two to three weeks each year at camp in training. However during the Seven Years War, the War of American Independence and the Napoleonic Wars most of the militias were embodied on permanent duty usually elsewhere than in the county where they were raised. They could not however be sent overseas, although some regiments served in Ireland around 1800. Whilst the men were on permament duty, wives and families were paid allowances, frequently recorded in parish records. During the Napoleonic Wars additional units were raised by ballot as militia reserves, the Supplementary Militias, Army of Reserve and Local Militias. These men lived at home but with periods in training. They remained separate forces to the 'regular' militias, although the government tried every inducement after they had been trained to encourage them to transfer to the regulars, with varying degrees of success.

Also raised during the Napoleonic Wars were a multitude of local auxiliary forces, at their zenith during the invasion scares of 1798 and 1803-5, known variously as volunteer and fencible infantry, provisional, fencible and yeomanry cavalry, with associations and the pioneers and special constables raised under the Defence Acts. These units were not subject to military regulations but were controlled by the county lieutenancies. They could form and disband at will, whilst men could join and leave them as they wished. Most of the men were paid only whilst in training for a few weeks a year, living at home the rest of the time. Men serving in Associations were not paid at all, being equipped through money raised by public subscription (see subscribers list for Bath in Somerset). The equipment of the Provisional Cavalries, 1797-8, was funded by levies imposed on owners of riding and carriage horses (see Provisional Cavalry Levy Lists for Devon, Dorset and Lincolnshire).

The militia reserves and most auxiliary units were disbanded around 1816, and the regular militias returned to their peacetime status except for short periods when emergencies arose, such as in 1831 with the Reform Bill and agricultural riots. In

1859-60 a new generation of auxiliaries were formed, the Rifle Volunteers, and in 1881 they and the militias were linked to the regular army, mostly as militia and volunteer battalions of the county regiments.

The muster or pay lists for all units give few details other than names. Enrolment and Discharge lists however can be much more informative, occasionally giving places of residence, occupations and even ages.

Mervyn Medlycott

Further Reading

I.F.W. Beckett, *Riflemen Form: A Study of the Rifle Volunteer Movement, 1859-1908* (Ogilby Trusts, 1982).

I.F.W. Beckett, *The Buckinghamshire Posse Comitatus, 1798*, Bucks. Record Society **22** (1985). The introduction gives an excellent guide to this source and also covers the raising of the auxiliary forces, 1792-1803.

Dr Beckett has in preparation (for publication by Manchester University Press, 1990-1, a major study on the British Auxiliary Forces, including the Militia, Volunteers and Yeomanry for all periods.

R.P. Berry, *A History of the Formation and Development of Volunteer Infantry, 1794-1874* (1903). This also includes information on Local Militia.

J.W. Fortescue, *The County Lieutenancies and the Army, 1803-1814* (1909).

Victor A. Hatley, *Northamptonshire Militia Lists, 1777*, Northants. Record Society **25** (1973).

C. Sebag Montefiore, *A History of the Volunteer Force.*

J.R. Western, *The English Militia in the Eighteenth Century: The Story of a Political Issue, 1660-1802* (Routledge and Kegan Paul, 1965). Extensive footnote references.

Introductions to other publications cited under county sections usually provide detailed information on their respective sources. There are also, of course, numerous published histories of individual regiments and other bodies, of which County Local Studies librarians will be able to provide details.

BEDFORDSHIRE

Publications

'Size Roll of Major Richard Orlebar's
Company, Bedford, 29 May 1767', in
*Regimental Records of the Bedfordshire
Militia 1759-1884*, by Sir John M.
Burgoyne, 1884, p.123.
'Recruiting of militia, **1798**', *Bedfordshire
Historical Record Society* **3** (1916).
Levee en Masse List: **1803**. Oakley parish
[Beds. C.R.O. HA.15], in 'The 1803
Volunteers', A.J. Weston, *Bedfordshire
F.H.S. Journal*, **6**, 7 (1988).

Bedfordshire Record Office, Bedford.

There is an unpublished TS Guide to *Army
Lists and Muster Rolls at Bedfordshire
County Record Office*, compiled by N.K.
Lutt, 1987 (available for consultation),
which forms the basis (by kind permission)
of the following information.

Militia Ballot Lists
1761. Unnamed parish (30) [R box 771].
1775. Husborne Crawley (37) [P.49/13/3/1].

Levee en Masse Lists
1803. Barford, Stodden, Willey Hds. (north
Beds.) (men, 17-55; misc.) (6,080) [HA
15/1-4 and AD 1975]. Oakley published.

Militia Enrolment Lists
1760. **Barford, Stodden, Willey Hds.** (90)
[OR.1871].
1760-64. Harrold and district. Men chosen
by ballot and substitutes (246)
[OR.2071/214, OR.1873, OR.1000].
1760-92. County. Officers, sergeants and
corporals. Chronological list [R box 771.
Book of orders, p.621] (300). No
references to private soldiers or parishes of
origin.
1763. County (entire). Muster lists, arranged
by hd., parish and also by company
(1,000+) [R. box 771].
1778-83. Bedford St. Paul. Service details,
all over county (270) [P.1/12/11 and
P.1/17].
1779-1811. Potton. Service records, mostly
local men (58) [P.64/17/1-4].

Bedfordshire R.O.: *Militia Enrolments* ctd.

c.**1804. Hds.** of **Biggleswade, Clifton,
Wixhamtree.** Men chosen by lot (230)
[PM.2688].
1816-31. Barford, Stodden, Willey Hds.
(400) [GA.2391-94].
**1821-22. Biggleswade, Clifton,
Wixhamtree Hds.** (40) [ST.1099].
1831. 'Capn. Higgins' Company'. Many
different parishes across county (50)
[HI.185].
1852-72. County. 18th regt. Light Infantry
Militia. Arranged by hd.; alphabetical order
by parish (5,000) [LCM 3/2-5. LCM 3/5
has an index to parishes].

Volunteers Enrolment Lists
1803-4. Potton and district. Capt. Matthew
Rugeley's company lists and muster rolls
(300) [X.202/88, 95, 106, 120-2, 129,
142-3].
1803-9. Northill and district, Bedfordshire
Volunteer Horse Artillery. Muster roll (200)
[HY.832].
1860-92. County. Bedfordshire Rifle
Volunteers. Annual rolls, incl. parish
(15,000+) [LCV 5/1-5; LCG 68].
1860-1901. Bedford town (2,000+)
[Bedfs. R.V. Muster rolls. X.550/6/1-2].

Public Record Office, Kew.

County Regimental Returns (names listed
without location in the county)
Militia: **1780-1876** [WO.13/99-126].
Supplementary Militia: **1803-15**
[WO.13/2475].
Local Militia: **1st, 2nd Beds.: 1808-16**
[WO.13/3408-9].

BERKSHIRE

Berkshire Record Office, Reading.

Militia Ballot Lists
1807. Shellingford. [D/P 109/17/1/1-6].
*c.***1808.** Sonning. [D/P 113/17/1/1-2].

Enrolment List
1797. Supplementary Militia: **Abingdon Sub-div.** (called out on exercise at Wantage)
[D/EP 4/05, p.13].

Public Record Office, Kew.

County Regimental Returns (names listed without location in the county)
Militia: **1780-1876** [WO.13/127-153].
Supplementary Militia: **1803-16**
[WO.13/2476].
Local Militia: **Berks. 1st-3rd: 1808-16**
[WO.13/3410-2].

BUCKINGHAMSHIRE

Publication
Posse Comitatus Lists: **1798, whole county**
(23,000) [Bucks. CRO L/P 15-16 and
British Library Stowe MSS 805-6] in *The Buckinghamshire Posse Comitatus, 1798,*
ed. Dr. I. Beckett, Bucks. Record Society
22 (1985). By hd. and parish. Very good
index, and introduction giving background
to the making of the *Posse Comitatus.*
Appx. I is a survey of other *Posse Comitatus* survivals in England and Wales.
Both Mss. originals incorporated together.

The British Library Manuscripts Collections.

Posse Comitatus Lists
1798. Whole county (23,000) [Stowe Mss.
805-6]. Published.

Bodleian Library, Dept. of Western Manuscripts, Oxford.

Militia Enrolments and Substitutes
1759. Newport Pagnall 3 Hds. (64) [MS.
D.D. Dashwood B.8/2/19a]; **Stoke Poges
Hd.** (86) [/20]; **Desborough Hd.** (also **n.d.**)
(70, 116) [/21, 3/1]; **Cottesloe 3 Hds.**
(70) [/22]; **Ashenden Hd.** (77) [/23];
Aylesbury (Cuddington, Haddenham,
Hartwell, Dynton only) (21) [/23];
Buckingham 3 Hds. (72) [/25].
n.d. Desborough Hd. [MS. D.D. Dashwood
F.2/3/1].

Buckinghamshire continued

Buckinghamshire Record Office, Aylesbury.

Militia Ballot Lists
1796. Aylesbury 3 Hds. (500) [L/Md
2/1-30].
*c.***1800. Aston Clinton, St Leonards, Stoke
Mandeville** (200) [L/Pd 3].
1806. Hartwell [Way Mss. D/W 88/10].
1831. Newport 3 Hds. (2,000) [L/Md 5/9].

Local Militia Ballot Lists (limited to men aged
18-30)
1810, 1812, 1814-15. Cottesloe (3 Hds.)
(600 each year) [L/M 14-18].
1813. Edlesborough, Dagnall, Pitstone,
Cheddington, Ivinghoe, Mentmore with
Ledburn, Whitchurch [L/M 15].

Posse Comitatus Lists
1798. County (23,000) [L/P15-16].
Published.

Levee en Masse Lists
1803. Bledlow, Dinton, Princes Risborough,
Wendover, Great Missenden, North
Marston [L/V2/1,4,6-7 and L/V 6/9].

Militia Muster and Enrolment Lists
**1779, 1785, 1788, 1793, 1797, 1803,
1807, 1825. Newport (3 hds.)** (also rolls
of men to fill vacancies for various years
1781-1828), arranged by parish (100 on
each list) [L/Md/5/1-7].
**1788, 1793, 1797-98, 1803, 1807.
Aylesbury (3 hds.),** arranged by parish
(100 on each list) [L/Md/1/1-7].
1813. Royal Bucks. or King's Own Militia.
Whole county, arranged by parish (600)
[L/M/1].
1812-16. Cottesloe Hd. Arranged by parish
(250) [L/M/2].

Yeomanry Muster and Enrolment Lists
1794. Armed Yeomanry, mostly **mid-Bucks.**
(150) [L/Y/1/1].
n.d. (early 19th cent.?). Bucks. Provisional
Cavalry. **Whole county,** arranged by
division (180) [L/Y/2/1].
1798, 1802, 1803. Aylesbury squadron.
Mid-Bucks., arranged by division (1803 list
includes ages and number of children)
(250) [L/Y/2/3,4,7].
1798-1812. Aylesbury troop attendance
rolls. Mid-Bucks., arranged by division (120
each year) [L/Y/3].
1799-1801. Aylesbury troop. Mid-Bucks.,
arranged by division (300) [L/Y/5/10-13].

Buckinghamshire continued

Hertfordshire Record Office, Hertford

Militia Ballot List
1758. Coleshill in Amersham [Mil 1].

Hampshire Record Office, Winchester.

Militia Ballot List
1781. Cheddington [10M52/6/18].

Public Record Office, Kew.

County Regimental Returns (names listed
without location in the county)
Militia: **1781-1876** [WO.13/178-204].
Transcript of **1831** [WO.13/198], listing
538 names *with* parish of residence and, if
a substitute, parish for which serving, in
possession of Alan Dell, 3 Swallow Lane,
Stoke Mandeville, Aylesbury, Bucks.. HP22
5UW.
Supplementary Militia: **1801-16**
[WO.13/2478].
Local Militia: Bucks. 1st, 2nd, 3rd: **1808-16**
[WO.13/3416-8].

CAMBRIDGESHIRE

Cambridgeshire Record Office, Cambridge.

Militia Ballot Lists
1757. Linton (170) [L95/28].
1792. Sawston (50) [334/056].
**1793-1803, 1805-09, 1811-20, 1822-28,
1831.** Ely and South Witchford Hds.
[Evans and Sons 283/].

Army of Reserve Lists
1803. Ely and South Witchford Hds. [Evans
and Sons 283/].

Posse Comitatus Lists
1798. Gamlingay [P76/7/2]; Landbeach
[P104/1/4] (both of men, 15-60, in
households with population census; copies
held by Cambridge Group for Population
Studies).

Public Record Office, Kew.

County Regimental Returns (names listed
without location in the county)
Militia: **1780-1876** [WO.13/205-232].
Supplementary Militia: **1798-1815**
[WO.13/2479].
Local Militia: Cambridgeshire: **1808-16**
[WO.13/3421]; ...and Isle of Ely:
1808-16 [WO.13/3422].

CHESHIRE

Cheshire Record Office, Chester.

Enrolment Lists, etc.
1803-14: Militia, **County,** by hd.; **1803-4:**
Supplementary Militia [MF.210/2: this
microfilm (of deposited original documents)
also contains a good deal of other
miscelleaneous militia material].

Tameside Local Studies Library, Stalybridge
Library, Trinity Street, Stalybridge, Cheshire
SK15 2BN.

Militia Ballot Lists: **1796-1804.** Dukinfield
township (par. Stockport) (720)
[PCA/DUK/16/1].

Public Record Office, Kew.

County Regimental Returns (names listed
without location in the county)
Militia: **1st Cheshire: 1781-1876**
[WO.13/308-34]; **2nd Cheshire:
1798-1800, 1853-76** [335-45].
Supplementary Militia: **1798-1816**
[WO.13/2483].
Local Militia: **Congleton, Chester,
Macclesfield, Stockport: 1808-16**
[WO.13/3429-32].

CORNWALL

Cornwall County Record Office, Truro.

Militia Ballot Lists
1761. Gulval [X173/68].
1816. North Petherwin [P167/15/2/1] (134).

Levee en Masse Lists
1803. Gulval (householders with numbers of
men aged 15-60) [X173/69] (162).
1803. Mabe, Mylor, Penryn borough, St.
Gluvias (miscellaneous) [EN 1819/1-4]
(156).

Militia Muster Lists or Rolls
1781, 1782. Kerrier Hd. Militia roll and
substitutes [DDX.534].
1798. East Hd. Parishes, substitutes
[DD,RD1491].
1799. North Cornwall [FS.3/637].
1807-31. Royal Cornwall regt.
[X.394/3-11].

Cornwall continued

Public Record Office, Kew.

County Regimental Returns (names listed
without location in the county)
Militia: **1st Cornwall: 1780-1876**
[WO.13/346-70]; **2nd Cornwall: 1798-99,
1853-56** [WO.13/371-73]; **Cornwall
miners: 1798-1876** (Cornwall and Devon
Miners, 1820) [WO.13/374-96].
Supplementary Militia: **Cornwall 1803-14**
[WO.13/2484]; **Cornwall miners:
1798-1814** [WO.13/2485].
Local Militia: **1st-5th Cornwall, Pendennis
Artillery, Stany Artillery: 1808-16**
[WO.13/3435-1].

CUMBERLAND

Cumbria Record Office, Carlisle.

Militia Ballot Lists
**1807, 1809-14, 1817-18, 1820, 1822,
1824-29, 1831. Allerdale Below Derwent
Ward** [Q/MIL].
**1806-12, 1814, 1817-20, 1822, 1824-29,
1831. Cumberland Ward** [Q/MIL].
**1806-07, 1809-14, 1817-20, 1822,
1824-29, 1831. Eskdale Ward** [Q/MIL].

Militia 'Liable' Books
**1811, 1813, 1820, 1824, 1826, 1831.
Allerdale Below Derwent Ward** [Q/MIL].
**1797, 1802-03, 1807-13, 1820, 1824,
1826, 1831. Cumberland Ward** [Q/MIL].
TS indexed transcript to **Carlisle 1797.**
**1797, 1802-03, 1813, 1820, 1824, 1826,
1831. Eskdale Ward** [Q/MIL].

Public Record Office, Kew.

County Regimental Returns (names listed
without location in the county)
Militia: **1780-1876** [WO.13/397-421].
Supplementary Militia: **1803-14**
[WO.13/2468].
Local Militia: **Carlisle 1808-16**
[WO.13/3424]; **Cumberland; Whitehaven
Artillery; Workington: 1808-16** [3442-4].

DERBYSHIRE

Derbyshire County Record Office, Matlock.

Militia Ballot Lists
1802. Bakewell [D.2057A/PO23].
1802. Killamarsh [D.267Z box 15].
1802. Newbold and Dunston townships
(Chesterfield parish) [D.2262.Z/PV.1,
parish vestry minute book].
1822. Monyash township (Bakewell parish)
[D.766.Z/Z.1].

Militia Enrolment Lists
1803, 1817, 1820, 1825. One volume
(2,750).
1762-1864. Papers concerning such men
(1,250).

Naval Volunteers
1795-1797. One volume (200).
1795. Papers concerning such volunteers
(110).

*Sheffield Record Office, Sheffield Central
Library.*

Militia Ballot List
1798. Foolow township (Eyam parish) [Bag
C.643/1].

Public Record Office, Kew.

County Regimental Returns (names listed
without location in the county)
Militia: **1st Derby: 1780-1876**
[WO.13/447-472]; **2nd Derby: 1803-05,
1854-76** [473-479].
Supplementary Militia: **1st Derby:
1803-1816** [WO.13/2488]; **2nd Derby:
1804-05** [2499].
Local Militia: **Derby, Belper, Chatsworth,
Chesterfield Scarsdale, Wirksworth:
1808-16** [WO.13/3449-53].

DEVON

Publication

Levee en Masse Lists: **1803. City of Exeter**
[D.R.O. E.C.A. Miscellaneous Papers, box
5], incorrectly titled Exeter Militia List,
1803, ed. W.G. Hoskins, pubd. Phillimore,
Chichester, 1972. 3,102 names, indexed.
Note this is not a Militia List, but a Levee
en Masse List, under the 2nd Defence Act,
July 1803, listing all men in the city, aged
17-55. The original papers include other
categories (see below).

Devon Record Office, Exeter.

Militia Muster Rolls
**1758-76, 1781, 1795, 1817. City of
Exeter** [Exeter City Official Records].
1792. Barnstaple. Return of Officers,
N.C.O's and privates of Militia
[G.2/E.9/292(g)].
1797-1804. Cullompton [52/1/4-5].
**1808, 1813-16, 1832, 1838, 1846-47,
1861, 1863-65, 1867-69, 1873. County**
[G.2/E.8/279].

Levee en Masse Lists
1803. City of Exeter (men, 17-55,
published; and men, 15-60, for parish of
Holy Trinity, and everybody for parishes of
St. Mary Steps and St. Paul) (4,000)
[E.C.A. Miscellaneous Papers, box 5].
1803. North Tawton (everybody: men
17-55, and miscellaneous) [2914A/PM
77-159].
1803. Pioneers: Washfield [49/9/1/730b];
Lustleigh [1987A/PO 69].

Local Militia Muster Rolls
1809-11. Sidbury (8th company of East
Budleigh regt.) [2096 A add/PM3].
c.**1814.** Company of East Budleigh regt.
[516 M/06].

Cavalry Muster Roll
1812-13. Tiverton troop, Royal 1st Devon
Cavalry [49/9/1/730 C].

Militia Ballot List
1817. Cullompton sub-div. [Z.17/3/38].

Volunteers Enrolment Forms
1852-62, 1867-68, 1871. County
[G2/E9/282].

North Devon Record Office, Barnstaple.

Militia Ballot Lists
1791. Barnstaple and **Pilton** [Barnstaple
Borough Archives, B.1, boxes 849-850].

North Devon R.O. continued

Provisional Cavalry Levy Lists
1797. Hds. of **Fremington, Hartland** and
Shebbear [Bideford Borough Records
R2379A/Z38/31].

Levee en Masse Lists
1803. Barnstaple (everybody) [3054A/PC1].

Public Record Office, Kew.

County Regimental Returns (names listed
without location in the county)
Militia: **1st (East) Devon: 1780-1876**
[WO.13/480-505]; **2nd (North) Devon:
1780-97** [506-29]; **3rd (South) Devon:
1780-1859** [530-52]; **4th Devon:
1798-99** [553-54]; **Devon Artillery:
1853-76** [555-59].
Supplementary Militia: **1st or East Devon:
1798-1816** [WO.13/2490]; **North Devon:
1798-1816** [2491]; **South Devon:
1805-15** [2492].
Local Militia: **Devon: 1st, East, East
Budleigh, Highbridge, North, Roborough,
Tavistock, Torridge: 1808-16**
[WO.13/3454-61].

DORSET

Publication

'Dorset Militia Lists and the Levee en Masse,
1757-1803', M.T.M. Medlycott,
The Greenwood Tree (Somerset and Dorset
F.H.S.) **13**, 3 (July 1988), pp.92-93.

Dorset Record Office, Dorchester.

Militia Ballot Lists
1757. Puddletown Hd. (225) [LA.3/1].
1787. Cranborne sub-div. (752) [LA.3/2].
**1796. Blandford, Cranborne, Dorchester,
Wimborne sub-divs.** (3,009) [LA.3/3-6].
**1798. Blandford, Shaftesbury, Sherborne,
Wareham, Wimborne sub-divs.** (5,852)
[LA.3/7-11].
**1799. Cerne, Sturminster, Wimborne sub-
divs.** (3,019) [LA.3/12-14].

Militia 'Liable' Books
1758. Dorchester sub-div. (2,153) [LA.4/1].
1759. Hasilor, Rowbarrow, Cogdean (pt.)
Hds., Poole Borough (762) [LA.4/2].

Dorset: *Dorset R.O.* continued

Militia Enrolments
1761-69, 1776-78. Dorchester sub-div.;
1761-64, 1769-71, 1774-77, 1783-86.
Sturminster sub-div.;
1776-81, 1784-89. Wareham sub-div.;
1761-64, 1767-85. Wimborne sub-div. [all
LA.1] (800 in all).
1759. Lyme Regis; 1763-78, 1782 Dorset
substitutes (250) [LA.5/1-4].
1779, Dorchester sub-div. (22) [LA.2/4].
1779. Substitutes: Dorchester, Sturminster,
Wareham, Wimborne sub-divs. [LA.5/5-8].
1780-1. Substitutes: Sturminster,
Wareham, Wimborne sub-divs. [LA.5/9-11].

Militia Discharges
1762. County (50) [LA.2].

Provisional Cavalry Levy Lists
1796. Whole County (1,500) [D.52/1].

Levee en Masse Lists
1803. Corfe Castle Borough (householders)
(204) [PE/COC/MI.33].
1803. Rowbarrow Hd. (everybody) (3,023)
[D.286/5 & Ph.747].

**Dorset County Museum, *High West Street,
Dorchester.***

Posse Comitatus Lists
1798. Fifehead Magdalen, Kington Magna,
West Stour (100) ['Dorset Album', 1,
p.55]; particulars of millers and bakers
[LB.1/1(a)].

Town Clerk's Office, Poole Town Hall.

Levee en Masse Lists
1803. Poole Borough (men, 17-55;
householders; evacuees; pioneers) (8,127)
[no ref.].

**Dorset Military Museum, *The Keep, Bridport
Road, Dorchester.***

Militia Enrolments
1812-31. County (3,000).

Militia Succession Books, Officers and NCO's
1799-1881. County.

Public Record Office, *Kew.*

County Regimental Returns (names listed
without location in the county)
Militia: **1781-1876** [WO.13/560-84].
Supplementary Militia: **1798-1814**
[WO.13/2493].
Local Militia: **Dorset East, West: 1808-16**
[WO.13/3462-3].

Co. DURHAM

Cleveland County Archives Dept.,
Middlesbrough.

Levee en Masse List
1803. Stockton (men) (500) [U/S/78].

**Tyne & Wear Archives Service, *Newcastle
upon Tyne.***

Local Militia Muster Rolls
1800-08. Derwent, Durham, Gateshead,
Newcastle, Percy tenantry, South Tyne,
Sunderland, Usworth and Wallsend
[T.W.A.S. 564].

**University of Durham (Dept. of
Palaeography & Diplomatic), *5 The
College, Durham.***

Durham Yeomanry Cavalry
1817-1822. List of men enrolled (with
signatures) [Baker Baker Papers, List, **6,**
66/195].

Note. There are no relevant records at the
Durham County Record Office.

Public Record Office, *Kew.*

County Regimental Returns (names listed
without location in county)
Militia: **1st (South) Durham: 1780-1876**
[WO.13/608-32]; **2nd (North) Durham:
1853-76** [633-37]; **Durham Artillery:
1853-76** [638-41].
Supplementary Militia: **1798-1816**
[WO.13/2495].
Local Militia: **1st, 2nd: 1808-16**
[WO.13/3468-9].

ESSEX

Essex Record Office, *Chelmsford.*

Militia Enrolment Lists (Musters)
1797-98. Chelmsford, Dengie and
Rochford sub-divs. (principals and
substitutes, by parish) [L/DCp 1/21A].

Militia Ballot Lists
1815-17, 1819-27, 1829. Chelmsford sub-
div. [L/DCr 1-13, 28, 30-34].
1813. All Saints, Maldon [L/DCr 35].
1815-16, 1818, 1820-27, 1829, 1831.
Dengie sub-div. [L/DCr 14-27, 29, 35-41].

Posse Comitatus List
1798. Rochford [D/P/129/17/1].

Essex continued

Note. No relevant records at Essex R.O., Southend branch.

Public Record Office, *Kew.*

County Regimental Returns (names listed without location in the county)
Militia: **Essex (East): 1780-1876** [WO.13/673-99]; **Essex (West): 1780-1876** [700-25]; Essex (South): 1798-1805 [726-30].
Supplementary Militia: **East Essex; 1805-15** [WO.13/2497]; **South Essex: 1805** [2498]; **West Essex: 1804-16** [2499].
Local Militia: **1st-5th: 1808-16** [WO.13/3474-8].

GLOUCESTERSHIRE and BRISTOL
(for Bristol see also under Somerset)

Publication
Militia Muster Roll: **Hds. of Brightwells Barrow and Bradley, 1797,** in *Bristol & Gloucester Archaeological Society* **64** (1943), pp.148-57. 82 names, as to residence, trade, age, height, physical description, for whom serving and for where ballotted.

Gloucestershire Record Office, *Gloucester.* (Daily charge made.)

Militia Muster Rolls etc.
1802-31. Bibury sub-div. Militia books, details of men serving [D.1070/VII/63-66].
1802. ?County. Returns of men enlisted as ballotted men or substitutes [L/R.1].
1803. S. Glos. Militia: list of men serving, incl. substitutes, Painswick, Stroud; **N. Glos. Militia:** list of men sworn at Stroud [D.4693/14]. Also incl. **1807: Severn Rifle Corps** (180) and **Longtree, Bisley** and **Whitstone Cavalry troop** (parishes given).
1804. Sodbury. Volunteers and militia men (77) [D.2071 E.51].

Supplementary Militia
1797. Brightwells Barrow and Bradley Hd. Balloted men and substitutes [D.194].

Gloucestershire: *R.O.* continued
Yeomanry Muster Rolls, etc.
1794, 1802-04. Malmesbury Yeomanry troop. Signed articles of enrolment, 1794; muster rolls, 1802-4 [D.1571 X.17].
1797-1828. Royal Gloucester troop of Yeomanry Cavalry. Minute book, incl. members' signatures, 1797; names, 1803. From 1807 mainly changes of membership and officers [D.4920/1].

Volunteers
1798-1802. Frampton-on-Severn. Transcript of muster roll [D.149 X17; MI 19].
1803. Tetbury Volunteer Infantry [D.566 Z.13]; Frethern and Stinchcombe [D.149 X.29/1].
1803-4. 20th Glos. Rifle Volunteers; **1852, 1858-75** [L/R.1].
1859. Forest of Dean Volunteer Rifle Corps [D.36 Z.2].

Levee en Masse Lists
1803-4. Whitstone Hd. (special constables) (1,100) [D.149 X.29/14-34].

Gloucester Library.

Volunteers
1803-08. Dursley, muster rolls (75-100 names each).

Bristol Record Office.

Militia Ballot Lists [all ref. M.1]
1768. City of Bristol, 11 wards (1,900).
1771. Bristol, all 12 wards (2,000).
1779. Bristol, all 12 wards (2,150).
Jan. 1780. Bristol, 10 wards (1,650).
Apl. 1780. Bristol, 11 wards (2,100).
1781. Bristol, Trinity and St. Ewens wards.
1782. Bristol, 11 wards (2,050).
1787. Bristol, all 12 wards (2,100).
1788. Bristol, all 12 wards (2,150).
Feb. 1790. Bristol, 12 wards (2,100).
Aug. 1790. Bristol, 11 wards (2,050).
1792. Bristol, 10 wards (1,950).
Mch. 1793. Bristol, 11 wards (2,000).
Dec. 1793. Bristol, 10 wards (2,000).
1796. Bristol, 9 wards (1,950).
1799. Bristol, 9 wards (1,600).
1802. Bristol, 10 wards (1,350).
1807. Bristol, 10 wards (2,850).
1810. Bristol, all 12 wards (3,658).

Supplementary Militia Lists
1799. Bristol, 10 wards (1,600) [S.1].

Glos. and Bristol: *Bristol R.O.* ctd.

Local Militia Lists
1809. Bristol, all 12 wards (2,000) [L.3]. TS
transcript (by wards), index of names.

Army of Reserve Lists
1803. Bristol, 10 wards (2,600) [M.1].

Public Record Office, *Kew.*

County Regimental Returns (names listed
without location in the county)
Militia: **1st (South) Gloucester: 1780-1876**
[WO.13/834-60]; **2nd (North) Gloucester:**
1781-1876 [861-888].
Supplementary Militia: **North Gloster:**
1798-1814 [WO.13/2504]; **South**
Gloster: 1798-1816 [2505].
Local Militia: **Cotswold, East, North, West:**
1808-16 [WO.13/3493-6].

HAMPSHIRE

Hampshire Record Office, *Winchester.*

Posse Comitatus Lists
1798. Men, 15-60: Cranborne township
(par. Wonston) and parishes of
Bedhampton, Cove, Crookham, Farlington,
Long Sutton, Shalden, Southwick,
Tunworth, Weston Patrick; Miscellanous
(millers, bakers, waggoners *etc.*):
Portsdown Hd. (incl. Bedhampton,
Farlington, Southwick) and parish of
Bishops Waltham [Q.22/1/2/5].

Local Militia Ballot List
1810. Bursledon [130.M.83/PC.1].

Muster Rolls
1834-9, 1852-3. North and South Hants.
Militia [LL.25-29].
1834-46. North Hants. Yeomanry Corps
[LL.100-1].
1860-68. Hants. Volunteer Corps (Rifle,
Mounted Rifle, Artillery, Engineers)
[LL.51-75, 91-99].
1860-66. Hants. Yeomanry Cavalry
[LL.102].
The various lists contain between 5 and 300
names.

Enrolment Lists
1853-82. Hants. Militia (Infantry, Artillery,
Engineers) [LL.31-2, 36-8, 42].

Hampshire continued
Portsmouth City Records Office.

Volunteers
1797-8. Portsmouth, volunteer and
victualling office lists (artillery *etc.*)
[29A/1-8].

Southampton City Record Office.

Militia Ballot Lists
1825, 1826. Southampton Borough,
complete [D/PM 7/2/1.2].
1827. Portswood tithing [D/PM 7/2/3].
1828. Southampton Borough, 9 wards
[D/PM 7/2/4-12].
1831. Southampton Borough (part) [D/PM
7/3/2].

Service Papers
1788-1814. Southampton. Consents of
enlisted men (1 bundle).
1820-31. Southampton. Oaths and
substitutes' enrolments and medical
certificates (196) [D/PM.7/5/1-7].

Public Record Office, *Kew.*

County Regimental Returns (names listed
without location in the county)
Militia; **Hants. (North): 1792-1876**
[WO.13/891-914]; **Hants. (South):**
1780-1853 [915-934]; **Hants. Artillery:**
1853-76 [935-40]; **Isle of Wight:**
1780-1876 [941-63].
Supplementary Militia: **North Hants.:**
1803-14 [WO.13/2506]; **South Hants.:**
1798-1815 [2507]; **Isle of Wight:**
1798-1816 [2508].
Local Militia: **South East, South West:**
1808-16 [WO.13/3498-9].

HEREFORDSHIRE

Note. There are no relevant records at the
Hereford branch of the Hereford and
Worcester Record Office.

Public Record Office, *Kew.*

County Regimental Returns (names listed
without location in the county)
Militia: **1780-1876** [WO.13/964-87].
Supplementary Militia: **1798-1816**
[WO.13/2509].
Local Militia: **1st, Archenfield, 1st and 2nd**
North: 1808-16 [WO.13/3500-3].

HERTFORDSHIRE

Publications
The Hertfordshire Family and Population
History Society is transcribing and
publishing the outstanding series of *Militia
Ballot Lists* that survive for the county
[Herts. C.R.O. Mil 1]. Published to date:
1. Hemel Hempstead (£2.00).
2. Sandridge, Ayot St. Peter and Ayot St.
   Lawrence (£2.25).
3. St. Albans St. Peter's (£3.05).
4. St. Albans Holywell Ward (£3.05).
5. Offley (£2.25).
6. Lilley and Hexton (£2.00).
7. Pirton and Ickleford (£2.50).
8. Stevenage (£3.30).
9. Great Amwell (£3.00).
Transcribed and awaiting publication: **Little
Amwell, Sacomb, Stapleford, St.
Margaret's.**
Transcription in progress: **Sleap and
Smallford, St Stephen's, Ware** and
Watford.
See Hertfordshire F.H.S. *Journal* **34**
(Summer 1988), 'Hertfordshire Militia
Lists', by J. Hill.
Radwell, 1758-86 (67), published in
Hertfordshire People (Herts. F.H.S.), **13**
(Summer 1981). Names arranged
alphabetically.

Hertfordshire Record Office, *Hertford.*

Militia Ballot Lists
Note. The county has the finest surviving set
of these Lists, which the relative brevity
and conciseness of this entry should not be
allowed to disguise. The arrangement is by
parishes and chronologically within each.
1758-66, 1768-9, 1772-3, 1775, 1777-87
[MIL 1]. Most of **County** (of these only
1764 is complete for the entire county,
though most other years have 90 per cent
or more of parishes surviving). Alphabetical
index of parishes with years covered. Some
transcripts, some published. There is a
transcript of Sandridge, 1758-86, at the
Society of Genealogists.
1792-4, 1796-8, 1801. Hertford and
Braughing Hds., various parishes [Mil 1].

Militia 'Liable' Books
**1759-62, 1764-5, 1768-9, 1772-3, 1775,
1777-87, 1793-8, 1803-4. Hertford** and
Braughing Hds. [Mil 1].

Hertfordshire R.O. continued

Muster Rolls
1759-61. Men serving in each company of
the battalion of Militia belonging to the
County of Hertford. Arranged by companies
and parishes within each (500) [D/EP
F.269].
1760-65. Men serving in Militia for **Hds.**
(sub-divs.) of **Cashio, Edwinstree, Odsey,
Dacorum.** Arranged by parishes [Mil 9/5,
11, 12, 15].

Volunteers
1798-1816. Hitchin [unlisted].
1808-22. County, Volunteer Corps [Mil 9].

Public Record Office, *Kew.*

County Regimental Returns (names listed
without location in the county)
Militia: **1780-1876** [WO.13/988-1011].
Supplementary Militia: **1799-1814**
[WO.13/2510].
Local Militia: **East, Midland, Western:**
1808-16 [WO.13/3504-6].

HUNTINGDONSHIRE

Note. There are no relevant records at the
Huntingdon branch of the Cambridgeshire
County Record Office.

Public Record Office, *Kew.*

County Regimental Returns (names listed
without location in the county)
Militia: **1780-1876** [WO.13/1016-38].
Supplementary Militia: **1803-14**
[WO.13/2511].
Local Militia: **1808-16** [WO.13/3507].

KENT

Kent Archives Office, *Maidstone.*

Militia Muster Rolls
1760. Faversham (150) [Fa/CPm 53].
1797-8. Cranbrook sub-div. [U.477 01].
1807-28. Lower part of southern div.: **Lathe of Aylesford** and **sub-div. of Woodgate** (500) [U.249 02(1)].
*c.***1850.** Rochester company [U.311/Z 3].

Militia Ballot Lists
1757. Sub-divs. of **Bearsted, Blackheath, Canterbury, Chatham, Cranbrook, Dartford** and **Sevenoaks; Hds.** of **Brenchley** and **Larkfield;** parishes of Goodneston (near Wingham), Lamberhurst and Monkton, borough of Queenborough (10,500 names, incl. 1,253 for Deptford and Greenwich, giving ages) [L/M.1].
1762. Barham, Bishopsbourne, Kingstone and St. Nicholas at Wade (258) [L/M.4].
1764-85 (every year). **Wingham sub-div.** (1,600 each year) [L/M.4].
1782, 1810. Kenardington (47) [P.206/17/1-2].
1785. Blackheath, Charlton, St. Nicholas Deptford, St. Paul Deptford, Eltham, Greenwich, Lewisham and Woolwich (1,900) [L/M.2].
1796, 1799, 1801-2. Dymchurch; and, **1799** only, Burmarsh (87) [P.125/17/1].
1802. Canterbury sub-div. (2,300) [L/M 3/1].
1817, 1831. Maidstone (1831 incomplete) (2,840) [P.241/17/2-3].
1821. St. Margaret Rochester (800) [P.305/17/1].
1828, 1831. Staplehurst (452) [P.347/17/1].

Army of Reserve Lists, 1803
Canterbury sub-div. (1,600) [L/M 3/2].
Deal borough (1,170) [De/ALI 1].
Burmarsh, Dymchurch, Eastbridge (39) [P.125/17/1].
St. Clement Sandwich, St. Peter Sandwich (226) [Sa/ALr 1-5].

Levee en Masse Lists, 1803
Deal borough (men, 17-55) (1,057) [De/ALI 2/1-3].
St. Clement Sandwich, St. Mary Sandwich, St. Peter Sandwich (men, 17-55) (477) [Sa/ALr 1-5].
Tenterden (incomplete: householders and men, 17-55) (36) [U.442/040/7].

Kent A.O. *continued*

Volunteers
1852-58. West Kent Militia [L/M 6].
1852-60. East Kent Militia [L/M 7].
1853-58. Kent Artillery Regt. of Militia [L/M 8].
1860-70. 15 Kent Rifle Volunteer Corps (105) [U.120 07].

Yeoman Cavalry
1843-47. East Kent (80) [U.373 C.3].

Kent Archives Office (South East Kent Area), *Folkestone.*

Levee en Masse Lists, 1803
Folkestone borough (householders; men, 15-60; men, 17-55; evacuees, pioneers and miscellaneous) [Folkestone Borough Records CPm 6-9].

Greenwich Local History Library.

Militia Books
1763-1808. Contents not ascertained.

Public Record Office, *Kew.*

County Regimental Returns (names listed without location in the county)
Militia: **Kent (East):** 1780-1876 [WO.13/1056-81]; **Kent (West):** 1780-1876 [1082-1107]; **3rd Kent:** 1798-99 [1108-9]; **Kent Artillery:** 1853-76 [1110-13].
Supplementary Militia: **Kent, east:** 1798-1814 [WO.13/2513]; **Kent, West:** 1798-1816 [2514].
Local Militia: **Deal Cinque Ports:** 1808-16 [WO.13/3445]; **Bearsted and Malling, Blackheath, Charlton and Dartford, 1st East, 2nd East, Sevenoaks and Bromley, Weald of Kent:** 1808-16 [3512-8].

LANCASHIRE

Lancashire Record Office, Preston.

Militia Ballot Lists
1763, 1802, 1815, 1817. Clitheroe [MBC 671 and DDX 28/259, 207, 208].
1823. Amounderness sub-div. (2,000) [LXA 6].
1826. Preston (1,800) [LXA 7].

Militia 'Exempt' Books
No date, perhaps *c.*1826. **Preston** township (1,035) [LXA 5].

Militia Muster Rolls, etc.
1797. Enrolment list, **Amounderness sub-div.** (360) [LXA 3].
1803-31. Enrolment books. **Amounderness sub-div.** (6,000) [LXA 1]. **Leyland sub-div.** (5,000) [LXL 1].
1804-74. Nominal rolls, by individual regts. (5,000) [LN 1-10].
1809-27. Enrolment books by townships in sub-divs. (12,000) [LN 13/1-3].
1816. Additional enrolment to supply deficiencies, **Amounderness sub-div.** [LXA 4/1-2].
1820-70. Miscellaneous nominal rolls (1,000) [LN 15,17,18].

Volunteers for the Army and Navy, 1796-7 **Salford Hd.** [QDV 1/15(16)].
Returns by township for **Hds.** of **Amounderness, Blackburn, Leyland, Lonsdale South and North, Salford, West Derby** [QDV 1/9-19].

Bolton M.B. Archives Dept.

Militia Muster Rolls, etc.
1804-16. Bolton sub-div. Army Reserve, Militia, and Volunteers' Pay Rolls [MS.60-64].
1817-31. Bolton sub-div. Militia enrolment books [MS 65-66].
1805. Bolton Light Horse Volunteers at Preston. Muster roll [no ref.].

Liverpool Record Office.

Muster Rolls
1808-16. Prescot sub-div. (name. trade, place of abode) [356 PRE 1-8].
1808-9, 1811-16. St. Helens Volunteers enrolment [356 PRE 1-3].

Greater Manchester County Record Office.

Muster Rolls etc.
[In Egerton of Wilton papers, not fully catalogued, numbers involved unknown].
1766-84, 1793-94. Royal Lancashire Volunteers.
1778, *c.*1782. Royal Manchester Volunteers (72nd Regt.).

Manchester Central Library, Archives Dept.

Muster Rolls
1796. Barrowford Militia (100) [L1/40/3].
1804. Royal Lancashire Militia (partial, 500) [C17/3/105/2].

Rawtenstall District Library, Rawtenstall.

Militia Ballot List
1810. Rossendale (TS indexed transcript) (630).

Public Record Office, Kew.

County Regimental Returns (names listed without location in county)
Militia: **1st Lancashire: 1780-1876** [WO.13/1158-85]; **2nd Lancs.:** **1798-1876** [1186-211]; **3rd Lancs.:** **1798-1876** [1212-37]; **4th Lancs.:** **1798-1876** [1238-46]; **5th Lancs.:** **1855-76** [1254-58]; **7th Lancs.: 1855-76** [1259-62]; **Lancs. Artillery: 1853-76** [1263-68].
Supplementary Militia: **1st Lancashire: 1803-16** [WO.13/2517]; **2nd Lancs.:** **1803-16** [2518]; **3rd Lancs.: 1799-1815** [2519]; **5th** (*sic*) **Lancs.: 1798-99** [2520].
Local Militia: **Amounderness, Blackburn, Blackburn Town Div., Bolton, Leyland and Ormskirk, Liverpool, Lonsdale, Manchester, Middleton, Newton and Failsworth, Oldham, Prescott, Trafford and Hulme, Warrington, Wigan: 1808-16** [WO.13/3528-42].

LEICESTERSHIRE

Leicestershire Record Office, Leicester.

Militia Muster Rolls
1772. Hds. of Gartree, East Goscote,
Guthlaxton, Sparkenhoe; Borough of
Leicester (men chosen by lot as Volunteers
or Substitutes) [LM.4/1/1-5].
1792-94. County (all hds. and borough of
Leicester; lotted men and substitutes)
[LM.4/2].
*c.***1810.** Substitutes [LM.4/3].
*c.***1860.** Leicester regt., by companies
[LM.4/4].

Leicestershire Rifle Volunteers Muster Rolls
1861-62, 1880, 1884-86 [LM.4/6-11].

Public Record Office, Kew.

County Regimental Returns (names listed
without location in the county)
Militia: **1780-1876** [WO.13/1269-94].
Supplementary Militia: **1805-14**
[WO.13/2521].
Local Militia: **Leicester, Loughborough,
Melton Mowbray, West: 1808-16**
[WO.13/3543-6].

LINCOLNSHIRE

Lincolnshire Archives Office, Lincoln.

Holland

Militia Muster Rolls
1816-31. Spalding sub-div. Minutes incl.
lists of ballotted men, some with
occupations and/or ages [HQS].

Volunteers
1852-54. Lists, with occupation, age, height
and township [HQS].

Lincolnshire A.O. continued

Kesteven

Militia Muster Rolls
1810. South and **North Lincolnshire.** List of
men volunteered into line, parishes,
substitutes and place of residence when
enrolled [KQS].
1817. South Lincolnshire. As above [KQS].
1818-23. North Lincolnshire. As above
[KQS].
1817-23. Various sub-divs. Ballotted men,
substitutes [KQS].
1825. South Lincolnshire, oath rolls,
substitutes and ballotted men [KQS].

Local Militia Muster Rolls
*c.***1808.** Men ballotted and enrolled from
Bassingham, Blankney, Carlton le
Moorland, North Kyme, Thorpe Tilney,
Welbourne [KQS].
Provisional Cavalry Levy Lists
**1796. Aswardhurn, Boothby Graffoe,
Flaxwell, Langoe** and **Loveden
Wapentakes,** and **Lincoln County of City**
[KQS].

Militia Ballot Lists
1803. Boothby Graffoe and **Langoe
Wapentakes,** and **Lincoln County of City,**
in Lincoln sub-div.; **Aswardhurn, Flaxwell**
and **Loveden Wapentakes,** in Sleaford
sub-div. Original and amended lists [KQS].
**1824. Aveland, Beltisloe, Langoe,
Loveden, Ness** and **Winnibriggs and Threo
Wapentakes, Grantham Borough and
Soke,** and **Stamford Borough and
Liberties** [KQS].
**1828. Aveland, Aswardhurn, Beltisloe,
Boothby Graffoe, Langoe, Ness** and
**Winnibriggs Wapentakes, Grantham
Borough and Soke, Lincoln County of
City,** and **Stamford Borough and Liberties**
[KQS].

Militia 'Liable' Books
1825. Bourne sub-div.: Aveland, Beltisloe
and Ness Wapentakes, and Stamford
Borough and Liberties, incl. St. Martin,
Stamford; **Grantham sub-div.:** Winnibriggs
and Threo Wapentake, and Grantham
Borough and Soke; **Lincoln sub-div.:
Boothby Graffoe and Langoe
Wapentakes, and Lincoln County of City;
Sleaford sub-div.:** Aswardhurn, Flaxwell
and Loveden Wapentakes [KQS].

Lincolnshire: *A.O.* continued

Ballotting Cards
1831. Aswardhurn, Aveland, Flaxwell and **Loveden Wapentakes, Grantham** and **Stamford Boroughs** and **Lincoln County of City.** Names and numbers on cards in small packets for parishes within larger packets for wapentakes, *etc.* [KQS].

Lindsey

Militia Muster Rolls
1762. Men ballotted, giving parish, and substitutes. At present unfit for production [LQS].

Militia Ballot Lists
1793 and undated. Various parishes [LQS].
1797. Manley Wapentake. [LQS].

Provisional Cavalry Levy Lists
1796. Louth and **Spilsby sub-divs.** [LQS].
Posse Comitatus List
1798. Glentham [Glentham Par.23].

Municipal Buildings, Boston.

Holland

Militia Ballot Lists
1808. Skirbeck and **Kirton Wapentakes** [Boston Borough Records 19/D].
Note. There is no relevant material at South Humberside Record Office, Grimsby.

Public Record Office, Kew.

County Regimental Returns (names listed without location in county)
Militia: North: 1781-1876
[WO.13/1295-1320]; **South: 1780-1876** [WO.13/1321-48]; **3rd: 1798-1805** [WO.13/1348-52].
Supplementary Militia: **North: 1803-14** [WO.13/2522]; **South** [WO.13/2523]; **3rd** [WO.13/2524].
Local Militia: **Holland and Boston, Lindsey, Lindsey and Riston, Loveden, Stamford: 1808-16** [WO.13/3547-51].

LONDON and MIDDLESEX

Publication
1622-1806. 'Huguenots in Trained Bands of London and the Honourable Artillery Company' [from Hon. Artillery Co. MSS.], in *Proceedings of the Huguenot Society of London,* **15** (1955), pp.300-16. Lists men alphabetically with brief biography.

Corporation of London Records Office, Guildhall.

Muster Rolls etc.
1777. City of London Trained Bands. Mostly Defaulters, arranged by company, from Committee for Defaulters minute book (1,000) [Lieutenancy Box 22.3].
1799-*c.*1817. City of London. Allocation of privates to Royal West London Militia. Wards of Aldersgate Within and Without, Bread Street, Castle Baynard, Cheap, Cordwainer, Cripplegate Within and Without, Farringdon Within and Without, Queenhithe, Vintry, Walbrook. Arranged by parish within each ward (5,000) [Lieutenancy Box 22.6; 22.7].
***c.*1806-*c.*1817. City of London.** Allocation of privates to Royal East London Militia. Wards of Aldgate, Bassishaw, Bishopsgate Within and Without, Billingsgate, Bridge, Broad Street, Candlewick, Coleman Street, Cornhill, Dowgate, Langbourn, Lime Street, Portsoken, Tower. Arranged by parish within each ward (1,600) [Lieutenancy Box 22.8].
The Office also holds late 18th and early 19th century material of genealogical interest relating to: (1) raising of volunteers for the army and navy; (2) payment of charity money and poor relief to servicemen and their families; (3) discharge certificates *etc.* to register exemption of servicemen and families from the requirement that traders in the City should be freemen.
Note. It appears that the two Militia regiments were raised from volunteers, so probably no ballots were held.

Greater London Record Office, 40 Northampton Road, EC1R OHB.

Pay Lists
1802. Western regt., Middlesex Militia. Three monthly pay lists (Jan., Feb., Apr.; 730 names per list) [Acc. 377/1-3].

London and Middlesex: *G.L.R.O.* contd.

Militia Ballot Lists
1812. Enfield (part) (8) [L/13].
1814. 'Out' Ward, parish of St. George
Hanover Square, Westminster (150) [L/14].
1822. Exchange Ward, parish of St. Martin
in the Fields, Westminster (700) [L/87].
1828. City of Westminster, complete (9
parishes, 41 wards) (30,000) [L/88-96].
Note. This is one of the most impressive
survivals of these quasi-census lists.

Honourable Artillery Company Archives,
*Armoury House, City Road, London EC1Y
2BQ.*

The Honourable Artillery Company was
embodied in 1537, as the Guild or
Fraternity of St. George, by Letters Patent.
Sadly the early Muster Rolls were lost
during the Civil War. The Artillery Company
was reorganised from 1608 and its Muster
Roll (known as the 'Vellum Book') starts in
1611 and continues to 1682 (published).
From 1682 to date the Muster Rolls are
complete. The list of Members was printed
from the late 18th century on, but until
1862 only the officers were listed. As usally
both work and home address was given,
these can be a valuable source. They are
available in the Guildhall Library to 1945.
The original musters are being indexed with
the aim of producing a single consolidated
index, 1537-1907, but will not be
completed for many years. A total of about
30,000 names are covered by these
sources.
For a small fee and s.a.e. information can be
supplied about Members, to those tracing
ancestors who served in the Company. No
detailed research can be done as the
Archivist is part-time and heavily
committed. No personal research may be
undertaken.
Being a volunteer regiment, few personal
details are available apart from height and
age, birth dates are rarely known and age
has to be taken on trust. In the Victorian
period it is useful to consult the local
newspaper *The City Press*, since the bulk of
the membership were City businessmen;
details concerning their firms or their civic
life will often be given, as well as covering
news about the Company in great detail.

Note. There is no relevant (post-1757)
material at the Guildhall Library,
Department of Manuscripts.

Public Record Office, *Kew.*

County Regimental Returns (names listed
without location in county)
Militia: **London, East: 1796-1820**
[WO.13/1353-70]; **London, West:
1796-1820** [1371-88]; **London, Royal:
1820-76** [1389-95]; **1st (East) Middlesex:
1780-1876** [WO.13/1419-44]; **2nd
(West) Middlesex: 1780-1876** [1445-68];
3rd (Westminster) Middlesex: 1780-1876
[1469-73]; **4th (South) Middlesex:
1798-99, 1853** [1474-1501]; **5th (North)
Middlesex: 1798-99, 1853-76** [1502-09];
1st Tower Hamlets: 1797-1876
[2143-68]; **2nd Tower Hamlets:
1797-1876** [2169-93].
Supplementary Militia:
East London: 1805-14 [WO.13/2525];
West London: 1805-14 [2526];
East Middlesex: 1799-1816 [2528];
North Middlesex: 1798-99 [2529];
South Middlesex: 1798-99 [2530];
West Middlesex: 1798-1816 [2531];
Westminster: 1803-16 [2532];
1st Tower Hamlets: 1805-15 [2561];
2nd Tower Hamlets: 1805-16 [2562].
Local Militia: Apparently none.

Monmouthshire – *see with* **Wales.**

24

NORFOLK

Norfolk Record Office, Norwich.

Militia Ballot Lists
1759. Antingham (40); **1762. North Erpingham Hd.** 10 parishes (140); **1763.** Beeston Regis (7) [WKC 7/105, 404 x 5].
1765. North Erpingham Hundred (500; by parish) [WKC 7/106, 404 x 5].

Militia Muster Rolls
1760. 1st battn. of Norfolk Militia (*c*.15 names on each) [MS 2657, 3 A B].
c.**1799.** 3rd regt. of Norfolk Militia sub-division book (register of soldiers showing age, place of birth, parish *etc*.). By hd. [MC 36/147, 481 x]. Temporarily withdrawn by depositor; not presently available.

Levee en Masse Lists
1803-4. Great Yarmouth, 2nd North Midds. only [mf 103/3; original in private hands].

Public Record Office, Kew.

County Regimental Returns (names listed without location in the county)
Militia: **1st (West) Norfolk: 1780-1876** [WO.13/1560-85]; **2nd (East) Norfolk: 1780-1876** [1586-1610]; **3rd Norfolk: 1798-99** [1611-12]; **Norfolk Artillery: 1853-76** [1613-17].
Supplementary Militia: **Norfolk East: 1803-14** [WO.13/2535]; **Norfolk West: 1801-16** [2536].
Local Militia: **East 1st-3rd, West 1st-3rd: 1808-16** [WO.13/3562-7].

NORTHAMPTONSHIRE

Publications
Militia Ballot Lists: 1762, Nassaburgh Hd. (Soke of Peterborough) [Nhants. R.O. X 1388-94], in 'Nassaburgh Militia Lists 1762', ed. Victor A. Hatley and Brian G. Statham, *A Northamptonshire Miscellany*, Nhants. Record Society **32** (1983), pp.107-46. By parish (1,286 names, indexed).
1777, County (excl. Nassaburgh Hd. (Soke of Peterborough) [N.R.O. X 1391-93], in *Northamptonshire Militia Lists, 1777*, ed. Victor A. Hatley, N.R.S. **25** (1973). By parishes within hds. (13,741 names, indexed). Good introduction.

Northamptonshire Record Office, Northampton.

Militia Muster Rolls
1766. Kettering div. (Corby, Rothwell, Huxloe Hds.) [X.268].
1786-7. Northampton div. (Spelhoe, Wymersley, Newbottle) [X.268].
c.**1798. Peterborough and Wellingborough divs.** [X.280/11, 284/15].

Militia Ballot Lists
Note. Northamptonshire has one of the best collections of these quasi censuses, for the years **1762, 1771, 1774, 1777** (published), **1781** and **1786.** Years surviving for each hundred are shown below. They are all referenced 'X 1388-94'; searchers are requested to give details of parish and year.

Chipping Warden. 1762, 1771, 1774, 1777, 1781.
Cleyley. 1777, 1781.
Corby. 1762, 1771, 1774, 1777, 1781.
Fawsley. 1771, 1774, 1777.
Greens Norton. 1762, 1771, 1774, 1777, 1781.
Guilsborough. 1771, 1774, 1777.
Hamfordshoe. 1762, 1771, 1774, 1777, 1781.
Higham Ferrers. 1762, 1771, 1774, 1777, 1781.
Huxloe. 1762, 1771, 1774, 1777, 1781.
Kings Sutton. 1762, 1771, 1774, 1777, 1781.
Nassaburgh. 1762. Published.
Navisford. 1762, 1771, 1774, 1777, 1781.
Nobottle Grove. 1771, 1774, 1777, 1781, 1786.
Orlingbury. 1771, 1774, 1777, 1781.

Northamptonshire: *R.O.:*
Militia Ballot Lists continued

Polebrook. 1762, 1771, 1777, 1781.
Rothwell. 1762, 1771, 1774, 1777, 1781.
Spelhoe. 1771, 1774, 1777, 1781, 1786.
Towcester. 1777, 1781.
Wymersley. 1771, 1774, 1777, 1781, 1786.
Willybrook. 1762, 1771, 1774, 1777, 1781.

1802, 1805, 1806, 1808-1828.
 Towcester div. (Cleyley and Towcester Hds.) [No ref.; quote parish and year].
 1803. Kettering div. (Corby, Huxloe and Rothwell Hds.) [X 281/3].

Posse Comitatus Lists, 1798
Blisworth, Brafield, Denton, East Haddon, Floore, Great Houghton, Grendon, Milton, Teeton, Upper Heyford, Weston Favell (men, 15-60, and miscellaneous) [X.269/1-1 to 11]. General index.
Abington, Brockhall, Bugbrooke, Church Brampton, Dallington, Duston, Horton, Nether Heyford, Overstone, Yardley Hastings (men, 15-60 and miscellaneous) [X.269/2-1 to 11].

Public Record Office, *Kew.*

County Regimental Returns (names listed without location in the county)
Militia: **1st Northants.: 1780-1856** [WO.13/1618-38]; **2nd Northants.: 1798-99** [1643-44]; **Northants. and Rutland: 1856-76** [1639-45].
Supplementary Militia: **1803-14** [WO.13/2537].
Local Militia: **Centre, East, West: 1808-16** [WO.13/3568-70].

NORTHUMBERLAND

Northumberland County Record Office, *North Gosforth.*

Muster Rolls
1745. Hexham militia rolls for the North Tyne, South Tyne and Hexham companies (200 names, by company) [ZAL. 98/5].
1774. Morpeth. Substitutes only (25) [ZBS. 4/2].
1797-1823. Muster rolls of Northumberland Volunteer Corps (many regts., full list at N.R.O.), covering whole of **County,** by company and within this by parish (50,000) [NRO. 1812/15-21]. Consisting of 7 bound folio volume on large sheets.
1798. Coquetdale, Morpeth, Glendale Wards. Supplementary militia (100). Also volunteers: **County,** by wards and parishes (500) [NRO. 1812/1].
1799. Northumberland Militia, 2nd regt. (1,250 names alphabetically by company; no parishes mentioned) [ZAN. M.12/C.22].
1799-1806. North Northumberland (from Alnwick northwards), Royal Cheviot Legion and Coquetdale Rangers (1,000, by parish) [ZAN. M.13/A.12].
1800. Wooler and district. Royal Cheviot Legion, Captain Hughes' Company (50) [ZSI. 355].
1803. North Tyne Volunteers, mainly Wark and Simonburn (82) [ZAL. 84/11].
1875. Northumberland Volunteer Corps: Hexham and Berwick parishes (400); also **1892: County** incl. Newcastle and Tynemouth, by particular volunteer corps (5,000) [ZGI. L Parcel III].

Militia Ballot Lists
1762. Whole County (12,000) [TS. transcript and Mf. copy, ref. M46]. Index to places. From original in possession of Duke of Northumberland

Posse Comitatus Lists
1798. Bamburgh, Castle, Coquetdale, Glendale, Morpeth Wards [QSB 90].

Levee en Masse Lists
1804. East div., Morpeth ward (special constables) [ZSW 602].

Navy Quota Act Returns
1796. Berwick upon Tweed, Glendale, Bamburgh, Coquetdale, Castle, Tindale, Morpeth, Newcastle upon Tyne (probably only one name per parish; details incl. in N.R.O. personal names index) [QAN].

Northumberland continued

Tyne & Wear Archives Service, Newcastle upon Tyne.

Local Militia Muster Rolls
1800-08. Derwent, Durham, Gateshead, Newcastle, Percy tenantry, South Tyne, Sunderland, Usworth and Wallsend [T.W.A.S. 564].

Public Record Office, *Kew.*

County Regimental Returns (names listed without location in the county)
Militia: **1st Nhumbd.: 1780-1876** [WO.13/1645-69]; **2nd Nhumbd.: 1798-99** [1670-71].
Supplementary Militia: **1798-1814** [WO.13/2538].
Local Militia: **Northumberland, Northumberland West, South: 1808-16** [WO.13/3571-3].

NOTTINGHAMSHIRE

Note. The terms 'Hundred' and 'Wapentake' appear to be used interchangeably in this county. For convenience, we have standardised on 'Hd.'

Nottinghamshire Archives Office, Nottingham.

Muster Rolls
1788-1803. Welbeck militia. Incl. lists [DD.4P 58/59-66].
1816-28. Yeomanry Cavalry. Various troops [LT/1/26-31].
1828-64. South Notts. Yeomanry Cavalry [LT/1/32].
1828-30. Sherwood Forest Rangers Yeomanry Cavalry [LT/1/36,38,39].
1860-92. 1st and 2nd Notts. Rifle Volunteers [LT/1/1-2].
1860-79. 3rd-8th Rifle Volunteers [LT/1/3-8].

Public Record Office, *Kew.*

County Regimental Returns (names listed without location in the county)
Militia: **1780-1876** [WO.13/1677-1701].
Supplementary Militia: **1803-13** [WO.13/2539].
Local Militia: **1st-4th: 1808-16** [WO.13/3574-7].

OXFORDSHIRE

For publication
Militia Ballot List: **1831. Bullingdon sub-div.** (City of Oxford; Bullingdon, Dorchester and Thame Hds.) (3,400) [Oxfordshire Archives L/M II/vii/2]. Transcribed by J.S.W. Gibson for publication by Oxfordshire F.H.S.

Oxfordshire Archives, Oxford.

Muster Rolls
1803. Watlington div., Oxfordshire Yeomanry Cavalry (83) [L/M X/i/i].
1803-07. Ploughley Hd. [Misc. Harding I/1].
1807-25. Bullingdon or Oxford sub-div., militia; also local militia, **1811-16** [L/M II/iii/1].
1817-31. Militia enrolments; also muster rolls, Oxfordshire Yeomanry Cavalry, **1816-20** [L/M VI/i/1].
1831. County (8 sub-divs.). Names of principals and substitutes; parishes of substitutes given for Bullingdon, Oxford, Watlington [L/M VI/iii/2].
1831. 1st Regt. of Oxfordshire Yeomanry Cavalry: NCOs and privates exempt from militia ballot [L/M VI/ii/1].
1852. Militia volunteers [L/M VI/i/2].
1860-62. 1st-9th Corps of Oxfordshire Rifle Volunteers (780) [L/M X/ii/1]; **1863-74** [L/M X/iv/1].
1875-92. 1st and 2nd Oxfordshire Rifle Volunteer Corps (later 1st and 2nd Battalions of Oxon. Light Infantry) [L/M X/iv/2].
1864-68. 1st Oxfordshire Light Horse Volunteer Corps [L/M X/iv/3].

Militia Ballot Lists
1831. Bullingdon sub-div. (Bullingdon, Dorchester, Thame Hds. and City of Oxford) (3,400) [L/M II/vii/2]. For publication by Oxfordshire F.H.S.

Bodleian Library, Dept. of Western Manuscripts, Oxford.

Volunteers
1803-9. Bicester independent company of infantry. Oath roll (200) [MS, Top. Oxon. c.223].
1805. Watlington div., Oxfordshire gentlemen and yeomanry cavalry [MS. Top. Oxon. c.290 f.11]; **Pyrton Hd.** company of volunteer infantry [f.14]; Oxfordshire yeomanry [f.21].

Oxfordshire continued

Public Record Office, Kew.

County Regimental Returns (names listed
without location in the county)
Militia: **1780-1876** [WO.13/1702-28].
Supplementary Militia: **1803-14**
[WO.13/2540].
Local Militia: **1st-3rd, East: 1808-16**
[WO.13/3578-81].

RUTLAND

Publication
Militia Muster Rolls: **1779-1783. County**
[Privately owned MS, in possession of the
transcriber, Dr. J.Perkins], in *Oakham
Marriages 1754-1837; The Rutland Militia
Rolls, 1779-1783*, Leicester University
Genealogical Society (1979). An
alphabetical list of 250 names, place,
occupation and if ballotted.

Note. There is no relevant material at the
Leicestershire Record Office. It is
understood that many of the Rutland Militia
papers are still in the custody of the Duke
of Rutland at Belvoir Castle.

Public Record Office, Kew.

County Regimental Returns (names listed
without location in county)
Militia: **1781-1856** [WO.13/1842-61]; after
1856 see 'Northampton and Rutland'.
Supplementary Militia: **1803-14**
[WO.13/2546].
Local Militia: **1808-16** [WO.13/3597].

SHROPSHIRE

Shropshire Record Office, Shrewsbury.

Militia Ballot List
1762. Ludlow Borough (419) [356/Box
299].

Militia Muster Rolls
1803, 1804. Bridgnorth (14); **Brimstree
South Hd.** (50); **Stottesden** (25)
[4001/Mil/1/Box 236].

Volunteers
Pre-**1806-8.** Loyal **Ludlow** Volunteer Infantry
(50, signatures on enrolment) [356/Box
299].

Shropshire continued

Public Record Office, Kew.

County Regimental Returns (names listed
without location in the county)
Militia: **1st Shropshire: 1780-1876**
[WO.13/1862-86]; **2nd Shropshire:
1798-1805** [WO.13/1887-91].
Supplementary Militia: **1805-14**
[WO.13/2547].
Local Militia: **Centre, North, South, West,
Wrekin: 1808-16** [WO.13/3598-602].

SOMERSET

Publication
Levee en Masse: **1803. Wiveliscombe** (367)
[Somerset R.O. DD/RI box 1]. Index in
Greenwood Tree (Somerset & Dorset
F.H.S.) **6**, 3, pp.62-63.

Somerset Record Office, Taunton.

Militia Muster Rolls and Enrolment Lists
1758. 1st Somerset regt. of Militia. List of
officers and men, with parishes [DD/SLI 1].
1799. 1st Somerset regt. Pay list and muster
roll [DD/SLI 2].
1822. Bath City and Bath Forum sub-div.
Principals and subs (250) [DD/CN 18/7].

Militia Ballot List
1770. Nynehead. (20) [DD/SF 3272].

Levee en Masse Lists, 1803
Bath Forum and **Wellow Hds.** 30 parishes,
with Hampton and Claverton Liberty, incl.
Bath City (mostly pioneers, some for men,
15-60, evacuees and miscellaneous)
[DD/RG 69-74].
Badgworth and Weare (men, 17-55) (95)
[D/P/badg/21/5/2].
Badgworth, Biddesham and Chapel Allerton
(pioneers) (63) [D/P/badg/21/5/3].
Radstock (householders) (170)
[D/P/rads/2/1/3].
Wiveliscombe (pioneers and miscellaneous)
(367) [DD/RI box 1]. Published index.

Yeomanry Cavalry Muster Rolls
1824, 1830. Bridgwater, Dulverton,
Wiveliscombe, Stowey, Dunster, West
Somerset, Langport, Milverton troops
[DD/CN 5/4]. Parishes given.
1830-1. North Somerset troop [DD/CN 5/4].
Parishes given.
1830. Mudford, Ilminster troops [DD/CN
5/4]. Parishes given.
1837. Mudford Independent [DD/CN 47/17].

Somerset continued

Bath City Record Office.

Association Subscribers' List
1792. Bath City (6,000). Ts. index.

Bristol Record Office.

Militia Enrolment Lists
**1765, 1768, 1771, 1776, 1777, 1779,
1782.** Hds. of **Portbury** and **Hartcliff with
Bedminster** (403) [AC/03].

Public Record Office, Kew.

County Regimental Returns (names listed
without location in the county)
Militia: **1st Somerset: 1780-1876**
[WO.13/1892-1916]; **2nd Somerset:
1798-1876** [WO.13/1917-40]; **Somerset
(East): 1798-99** [WO.13/1941-42].
Supplementary Militia: **1st Somerset:
1880-16** [WO.13/2549]; **2nd Somerset:
1803-15** [WO.13/1550].
Local Militia: **Bridgwater, East, Mendip East,
Mendip West, Polden Hill, Somerton and
Langport, West: 1808-16**
[WO.13/3603-9].

STAFFORDSHIRE

Note. The Staffordshire Record Office has no
relevant 18th and 19th century militia
records; nor do Lichfield Joint Record
Office, Walsall Local History Centre and
Wolverhampton Archives Department.

Public Record Office, Kew.

County Regimental Returns (names listed
without location in the county)
Militia: **1st Staffordshire: 1780-1876**
[WO.13/1943-70]; **2nd Staffs.:
1798-1805, 1851-76** [1971-82]; **3rd
Staffs.: 1798-1800, 1853-76** [1983-89].
Supplementary Militia: **1st Staffs.:
1798-1807, 1808-16** [WO.13/2551-2];
2nd Staffs.: 1803-15 [2553]; **3rd Staffs.:
1798-99** [2554].
Local Militia: **Central, East, North, South,
West: 1808-16** [WO.13/3610-4].

SUFFOLK

The British Library Manuscripts Collections.

Volunteers
1798. Parish of Yoxford in Blything Hd. (85,
who 'do agree to form themselves into an
Independent Company', headed by John
Lockwood, Chaplain) [Add. MSS. 19188].

Suffolk Record Office, Ipswich.

Militia Muster Rolls
1757. Bury div. Signatures of Militia men to
Oaths of Allegiance *etc.* [505/1/1].
1777. Eastern regt. of Suffolk Militia, Lt. Col.
Goates's company [HD.190/2].
Late 18th cent. (?). Great Bealings. 'A true
list of the military men' [FC.31/G.4/1].
1801 (or 1814). East Suffolk Militia.
[H.15/3/2.1]. Indexed.
1814-16. Men enrolled at Woodbridge
[H.15/3/2.2].
1853. West Suffolk Militia. Monthly return
and volunteers enrolled [HA.11/B12/22 and
HA.11/B.1/19/15].

Militia Ballot List
1778. Wickham Market (part) [52/15/20].

Note. There are no relevant 18th and 19th
century records at the Bury St. Edmunds
and Lowestoft branches of Suffolk R.O.

Public Record Office, Kew.

County Regimental Returns (names listed
without location in the county)
Militia: **Suffolk (East): 1780-1853**
[WO.13/2009-29]; **Suffolk (West):
1780-1876** [2030-53]; **Suffolk Artillery:
1853-76** [2054-58].
Supplementary Militia: **East Suffolk:
1803-16** [WO.13/2556]; **West Suffolk:
1803-14** [2557].
Local Militia: **East, 1st and 2nd West:
1808-16** [WO.13/3617-9].

SURREY

Publications

Militia Muster Rolls: **1759. Godalming, Farnham** and **Blackheath Hds.** (80, by parish) [Surrey R.O., Guildford: LM.1330/87], in *Root and Branch* (West Surrey F.H.S.) **8**, 3.

Early 19th cent. Mitcham parish (Brixton Hd.) [Surrey R.O.]. Alphabetical list of 190 names, some showing place of birth, residence and substitute information. 8pp. TS, pub. as East Surrey F.H.S. **34**.

1800-09. Mortlake Militia Records [Surrey R.O.]. 11 names only, as East Surrey F.H.S. **52** (1987).

The British Library Manuscripts Collections.

Levee en Masse List
1803. Seal and Tongham [Add. MSS. 45524 ff.21-30].

Surrey Record Office, Kingston.

Militia Ballot Lists
1763. Kingston upon Thames (259) [Kingston Borough Archives, KH.1/1/6].
*c.***1784.** Oxted [P.3/5/113].
1813, 1819. Bletchingley [2727/1/48/91].
1821. Ewhurst [2132/6/17].

Levee en Masse List
1803. Oxted (men, 17-55, and householders) [P.3/11/1-44].

Militia Muster Rolls
1794. Surrey Militia, Sir John Frederick's Company. Accounts, incl. alphabetical list [183/34/29].
n.d. 'Roll call', Wimbledon parish [P.5/20/2].

Surrey Record Office, Guildford.

Militia Muster Rolls
1759. Godalming, Farnham and **Blackheath Hds.** (80, by parish) [LM.1330/87]. Published.
1786, 1803. West Surrey (100 each, by parish) [51/21/2; 1/1/82].
1807-8. West Surrey (300, by parish) [1/1/83].
1810-27. Guildford sub-div. (1,000, by parish) [1478].

Lambeth Archives Dept., Minet Library, 52
Knatchbull Road, London SE5 9QY.

Militia Muster Roll
1803-04. Western Surrey (of those enrolled and their substitutes) [Surrey Deeds 1/6385].

Public Record Office, *Kew.*

County Regimental Returns (names listed without location in the county)
Militia: **1st Surrey: 1780-1876** [WO.13/2059-83]; **2nd Surrey: 1798-1876** [2084-106]; **3rd Surrey: 1798-99, 1853-76** [2107-12].

Supplementary Militia: **1st Surrey: 1803-16** [WO.13/2558]; **2nd Surrey: 1803-14** [2559].

Local Militia: **1st-5th: 1808-16** [WO.13/3620-4].

SUSSEX

Publications

Levee en Masse: **1803. Pevensey Rape** (6,419 men, 17-55) [East Sussex R.O. LPL/1/E.1-4], as *Sussex Militia Lists 1803: Southern Division* (32 parishes), £3.65 incl U.K. p&p, £4.10 surface o'seas; *Northern Divison* (19 parishes), £4.25 U.K., £4.96 surface o'seas. Published 1988 by PBN Publications, 22 Abbey Road, Eastbourne, Sussex BN20 8TE. Names arranged alphabetically within each parish.

East Sussex Record Office, *Lewes.*

Militia Ballot Lists
1797. Rottingdean [BRD 4/1].
1801-03, 1824. Icklesham [Par 401 36/8(2), /9, /12(1), /18].
1802. Ewhurst [Par 324 36/11].
1810. Laughton (part) [Par 409 36/11,12].
1816. Buxted [LPL/4/E.1].
1824. Ovingdean [Par 436 36/1].
1825. Pevensey Rape, southern half (32 parishes) [LPL/4/E.2]
1826, 1827. Hartfield [Par 360 36/8,9,10].

Posse Comitatus List
1798. Icklesham (men, 15-60) [Par 401 36/3/1-3].

Levee en Masse Lists, 1803
Pevensey Rape (51 parishes; 6,419 men, 17-55) [LPL/1/E.1-4]. Published.
Ewhurst (men, 17-55) [Par 324 36/23].
Icklesham (men, 17-55) [Par 401 36/10/1].

Army of Reserve Lists
1803-4. Pevensey Rape (51 parishes) [LPL/2/E.1-2].
1803. Ewhurst [Par 324 36/24]; Icklesham [PAR 401 36/11/1].

Sussex: *East Sussex R.O.* contd.

Volunteer Infantry
1803. South Lewes Regt., Captain Roberts'
Company (Hurstpierpoint parish return) (25)
[Ashburnham Ms.3349; photocopy at
W.S.R.O. MP 2429].

Local Militia Muster Rolls
1813. County(?) [LPL/3/E.1-3].

Militia 'Exempt' Books
1829. Brighton sub-div. [LBL/E.1].

West Sussex Record Office, Chichester.

Army of Reserve Enrolment List
1803-04. Arundel Rape (100) [R.S.R. Mss.
3/1-42].

Militia Ballot Lists
1813-16. Findon (320) [Add.Ms. 36,505].
1827, 1828. Rogate [Par 159/36/1].

Militia Muster Rolls
1808. Stedham [Par 182/36/1].
1820. Hurstpierpoint [Par 400/36/113].
1821-22. Bolney [Par 252/36/1].
1823-25. Rusper [Par 163/36/1-2].
1831. Arundel [Par 8/36/2].

Public Record Office, *Kew.*

County Regimental Returns (names listed
without location in the county)
Militia: **1780-1876** [WO.13/2113-38];
Sussex Artillery: 1853-76 [2054-58].
Supplementary Militia: **1798-1815**
[WO.13/2560].
Local Militia: **Central, East, Pevensey, West**
[WO.13/3625-8].

WARWICKSHIRE

Warwickshire County Record Office,
Warwick.

Militia Muster Rolls
1758. Hds. of **Hemlingford** and **Knightlow**
(lists men, but no other information)
[CR.136/C.1691].
1750s-1760s. Nuneaton Militia Company.
Incl. lists of men, heights, ages
[CR.136/B.5057-5156]. Not necessarily
complete.

Militia Ballot List
n.d., but under 1806 Act. Mancetter
[CR.911/18].

Warwickshire continued

Birmingham Reference Library, Archives
Dept.

Militia Ballot Lists
1810, 1819, 1821. Sheldon (117) [DRO 42
St. Giles Sheldon Box 4 Militia nos. 9-11].

Shakespeare Birthplace Trust Record
Office, *Stratford upon Avon.*

Militia Enrolment List
1807-8. Barlichway Hd. (75) [ER 42/1-3].

Note. There is no relevant 18th and 19th
century material at the Coventry City
Record office.

Public Record Office, *Kew,*

County Regimental Returns (names listed
without location in the county)
Militia: **1st Warwicks.: 1781-1797**
[WO.13/2194-2217]; **2nd Warwicks.:**
1803-05, 1852-76 [2218-27].
Supplementary Militia: **1st Warwicks.:**
1798-1813 [WO.13/2563]; **2nd**
Warwicks.: 1805 [2564].
Local Militia: **1st-5th: 1808-16**
[WO.13/3638-42].

WESTMORLAND

Cumbria Record Office, *Kendal.*

Militia Muster Rolls
1764. Kendal and **Lonsdale Wards** [WDX
194/Z.2]
1770. East and **West Wards** [WDX
194/Z.3].
1774. East, West, Kendal and **Lonsdale**
Wards [WDX 194/Z.4].
1852-3. Royal Westmorland Militia [WDY
35].

Militia Ballot Lists
1779. Ravenstonedale [WDX 94].
*c.***1830.** Mallerstang [WDX 3/9].

Public Record Office, *Kew.*

County Regimental Returns (names listed
without location in the county)
Militia: **1780-1876** [WO.13/2228-50].
Supplementary Militia: **1798-1814**
[WO.13/2565].
Local Militia: **Appleby, Kendal and Lonsdale:**
1808-16 [WO.13/3635-6].

WILTSHIRE

Publication
'Searching the Wiltshire Regiments of Militia, 1780-1814', Edward Lawes, in *Wiltshire F.H.S. Journal* 5 (Spring 1982), pp. 10-15.

Wiltshire Record Office, *Trowbridge.*

Muster Rolls
1757-61. West Wilts. Militia enrolments (200) [A.1/800]; substitutes [A.1/712].
1759-1771. County. Wiltshire Militia, various enrolment lists and musters (4,500). Also lists of officers, 1810-12, NCOs 1822-7 [9/Savernake].
1768. Melksham Hd. Substitutes (20) [A.1/810].
1773-1831. Calne and Chippenham area. Ballotted men and substitutes (several hundred) [137/123].
1795. County. Volunteers and substitutes under Navy Act (200) [A.1/545].
1797. North Wilts. Militia enrolments (several hundred) [84/41].
1807-8, 1812. Sarum sub-div. Enrolment lists, principals and substitutes, in County, Supplementary and Local Militias (740) [906/W.266-70].
1821, 1824-7, 1831. Marlborough sub-div. Enrolment lists, principals and substitutes [2027].

Levee en Masse Lists, 1803 [all 2039/1]
Nunton and Bodenham. Non-combatants and pioneers (86).
Stratford Tony. Non-combatants and pioneers (39).
Coombe Bissett. Non-combatants and pioneers (103).
Britford. Pioneers (21).
Marlborough St. Peter (264 men, 15-60) [871/212].
Box (331: men, 17-55; householders; miscellaneous, bakers, millers, waggoners etc.) [1719/30].

Public Record Office, *Kew.*

County Regimental Returns (names listed without location in the county)
Militia: **1st Wiltshire: 1780-1876** [WO.13/2251-80]; **2nd Wiltshire: 1798-1805** [2281-85].
Supplementary Militia: **1802-16** [WO.13/2566].
Local Militia: **1st-5th: 1808-16** [WO.13/3638-42].

WORCESTERSHIRE

Hereford and Worcester Record Office, St. Helen's, Fish Street, Worcester.

Militia Muster Lists and Returns
1799. Kidderminster Association of Infantry (60) [705:73 BA 3261/2(i)]. One list too fragile for production.
1799, 1805. Worcs. regt. of Militia (50) [705:73 BA 3261/2(i)].
1808-16. Worcs. Militia. Register containing 400 names of recruits, date of enlistment, age, place of birth, physical description and occupation [b.899:683 BA 9684].
1812. Worcs. regt. of Militia (32) [705:73/ BA 3261/5(iv)].

Militia Ballot Lists
1806-14. Hartlebury (1,000) [b.850 Hartlebury BA 9490/5(vi)].
1824, 1825, 1827-31. Kidderminster St. Mary (1,300) [850 Kidderminster St. Mary BA 4766/7(i)].

Local Militia Muster Roll
1812. Worcs. Local Militia assembled for exercise (700) [989.9:66 BA 857].

Volunteers
1803-4. Dudley Light Horse (15) [705:73 BA 3261/3(iv)].
1808. North Worcs. Volunteers (150). Incl. Alvechurch, Tardebigge, King's Norton, Feckenham, Bromsgrove, Birmingham, Solihull areas [705:73 BA 2868/6 (xxxii)].

Birmingham Reference Library, Archives Dept.

Militia Ballot List
1825. Yardley (300) [MS 387/51].

Note. There are no relevant records in Dudley Library Archives Dept.

Public Record Office, *Kew.*

County Regimental Returns (names listed without location in the county)
Militia: **1st Worcs.: 1780-1876** [WO.13/2286-2310]; **2nd Worcs.: 1798-1800** [2311-12].
Supplementary Militia: **1798-1816** [WO.13/2568].
Local Militia: **Worcester, East, North, South, West: 1808-16** [WO.13/3643-7].

YORK and the AINSTY

City of York Archives Department.

Note. Unless otherwise stated the lists cover the City of York and the Wapentake of the Ainsty.

Muster Rolls
1745. 'The Association' volunteers [E.130].

Militia Muster Rolls
Note. The York militia rolls, 1777-1825, are completely illegible due to flooding. Many of the names of those serving can be recovered from copy rolls and other documents, but there is a total gap for the years 1784-1808. None of the militia lists have been indexed, so unless a parish is known it is a lengthy process to find a name. Archives staff can only undertake searches on a pre-agreed charge basis.
1784, 1813-26. Some copy militia rolls [K.18].
1808. Lists of men enrolled (600) [K.16b].
1809-15. Account book re. substitutes (3,500) [E.75].
1801-26. Some draft lists [K.19].
1813. Lists of names enrolled (500) [K.16e].

Militia Ballot Lists
1829. York and Ainsty (2,000) [K,16e].

Public Record Office, Kew.

Regimental Returns
Local Militia: **York: 1808-16** [WO.13/3648].
Note. There are no relevant records relating to York and the Ainsty for the *Militia* and *Supplementary Militia,* 1780-1876. See under Yorkshire Ridings.

YORKSHIRE: EAST RIDING

Kingston upon Hull City Record Office.

Militia Ballot Lists.
1792, 1793, 1794, 1795. Kingston upon Hull Town only [CAM 10].
1794. Kingston upon Hull, town and county [CAM 10].
1823. Kingston upon Hull, eight townships in county [CAM 11-20].

The Borthwick Institute of Historical Research, York.

Muster Rolls
1745. Lists of companies of foot soldiers during the Jacobite rebellion (several hundred names) [Bp.C&P. XXI].

Yorkshire: East Riding continued

Public Record Office, Kew.

County Regimental Returns (names listed without location in the county)
Militia: **East Yorks.: 1780-1876** [WO.13/2313-37]; **East and North Yorks. Artillery: 1860-76** [2338-40].
Supplementary Artillery: **1803-15** [WO.13/2569].
Local Militia: **1st-4th: 1808-16** [WO.13/3650-3].

YORKSHIRE: NORTH RIDING

Publication
Posse Comitatus Lists. **1798:** Spennithorne, and **1801:** Langbaurgh East Wapentake [North Yorks. R.O.] in 'To Escape the Monster's Clutches', North Yorks. R.O. Publications **15** (1977).

The Borthwick Institute of Historical Research, York.

Muster Rolls
1745. Lists of companies of foot soldiers during the Jacobite rebellion (several hundred names) [Bp.C&P. XXI].

North Yorkshire County Record Office, Northallerton.

Posse Comitatus Lists
1798. Spennithorne [ZQH 11/3/166 and Mic 1168]. Published.
1801. Langbaurgh East Wapentake [ref.: L]. Published.

Public Record Office, Kew.

County Regimental Returns (names listed without location in the county)
Militia: **1st North Yorks.: 1780-1876** [WO.13/2341-66]; **2nd North Yorks.: 1798-99** [2367-8]; **East and North Yorks. Artillery: 1860-76** [2338-40].
Supplementary Militia: **1803-15** [WO.13/2570].
Local Militia: **1st-6th: 1808-16** [WO.13/3659-64].

YORKSHIRE: WEST RIDING

Publications

Volunteers: **1757, 1782-1814,** in 'The early Leeds Volunteers', by Emily Hargrave, *Miscellanea 9,* Thoresby Soc. **28** (1928).

Volunteers: **1794-5.** 'The Enrolment Lists of the Loyal Independent Sheffield Volunteers', in *The Flowing Stream* (Sheffield F.H.S.), **2** (1980).

Levee en Masse Lists: **1803. Staincliffe with Ewcross Wapentake** (9,000 names, by parish and occupation) [North Yorks. R.O.], in *The Craven Muster Roll,* North Yorks. R.O. publication **9** (1976).

Volunteers: **1820,** in 'The Leeds Volunteers, 1820', by Emily Hargrave, *Miscellanea 7,* Thoresby Soc. **24** (1919). 95 names and occupations 'who volunteered to assist the Civil Power.'

Bradford District Archives, *15 Canal Road, Bradford.*

Militia Muster Rolls
1793. First regt. of West Riding Militia (100 and 70) [Sp.St. 10/7/16,17].

Militia Ballot Lists:
1813, 1814. Tong (130, 120) [Tong 10/26,34].

Calderdale District Archives, *Central Library, Halifax.*

Militia Ballot Lists
1803. Heptonstall township (200) [HPC/A:55].
***c.*1806.** Sowerby township (500) [SPL:110/29].
1829. Stansfield (400) [TT:125].

Militia Muster Roll
1803-04. Halifax township, ballotted men (200) [VOL:1].

Local Militia
1801-13. West Halifax Regt., pay lists (60 each) [FH:347].
1813. Sowerby township, in West Halifax Regt. (37) [SPL:329].

Volunteers
1801-13. West Halifax, pay lists (60 each) [FH:347].

Yeomanry Cavalry
1843-78. Agbrigg and Morley Wapentake. Thrice annual muster rolls (60 each) [Misc:150].

Kirklees District Archives, *Central Library, Huddersfield.*

Militia Ballot Lists
1796-98. Thurstonland township (200) [KC.271/54, /55, /58].

Leeds District Archives, *Chapeltown Road, Sheepscar, Leeds.*

Militia Muster Rolls
1817. Skyrack Wapentake and **Leeds Borough** (840) [DB 264/2].
1822. Wapentakes of Claro (440) [DB 264/3]; **Osgoldcross** (240) [DB 264/4].

Doncaster Archives Department, *King Edward Road, Balby, Doncaster.*

Militia Ballot Lists
1796-1831 (23 surveys). Swinton (2,000; 37-196 in each) [P.59/6/C.3/1,2].
1822-1831 (17 surveys). Snaith (1,300; 50-100 in each) [P.50/6/C.1/1].

Sheffield Record Office, *Central Library, Sheffield.*

Militia Ballot Lists
1796-1800, 1803-04, 1817-20, 1822-29, 1831. Swinton (2,000) [Ph.C.454-477; photocopies of originals at Doncaster Archives Dept., see above].
1814, 1815. Hooton Roberts [PR 26/27].
1819-29, 1831, Bradfield [Ph.C. 442 (1-12), photocopies].

North Yorkshire County Record Office, *Northallerton.*

Levee en Masse Lists
1803. Staincliffe with Ewcross Wapentake (9,000 men, 17-55) [Z.787]. Published.

Public Record Office, *Kew.*

County Regimental Returns (names listed without location in the county)
Militia: **1st West Yorks.: 1780-1876** [WO.13/2369-97]; **2nd: 1780-1876** [2398-2425]; **3rd: 1798-1876** [2426-51]; **4th: 1798-1800, 1853-76** [2452-58]; **5th: 1798-99, 1853-76** [2459-68].
Supplementary Militia: **1st West Yorks.: 1799-1816** [WO.13/2571]; **2nd: 1803-16** [2572]; **3rd: 1803-14** [2573].
Local Militia: **1808-16: Agbrigg** [WO.13/3649]; **Halifax, Halifax West, Leeds 1st and 2nd; Morley** [3654-8]; **Sheffield, Staincross, Strafforth and Tickhill, Wakefield, West Clar, West Craven** [3665-70].

WALES and MONMOUTHSHIRE

ANGLESEY

Anglesey Area Record Office (Gwynedd Archives), Llangefni.

Militia Ballot Lists
1810-11, 1825. Hds. of **Dindaethwy, Menai** and **Malltraeth** [WQS/Militia].
1823. Leifin Hd. [WQS/Militia].

Militia Enrolment Lists
n.d. County (ballotted men and substitutes, with occupations, parishes, number of dependents).

Department of Manuscripts, University College of North Wales Library, Bangor.

Posse Comitatus List
1798. Beaumaris borough (men, 15-60) [Beaumaris Borough Records, I/309-324].

Public Record Office, Kew.

County Regimental Returns (names listed without location in the county)
Militia: **1780-1876** [WO.13/2650].
Supplementary Militia: **1803-14** [WO.13/2472].
Local Militia: **1808-16** [WO.13/3399].

BRECON or BRECKNOCK

The National Library of Wales, Aberystwyth.

Militia Muster Rolls [Tredegar Park]
1757. Merthyr Hd. [119/210].
1760. Crickhowell Hd. [119/211]; **Merthyr Hd.** [113/27].

Militia Ballot Lists
1798. Cathedin, Llaneleu, Llangors, Talgarth, Llandyfalle, Llanigon, Llyswen, Glasbury, Bronllys, Gwenddwr and Llangasty Talyllyn [Maybery Mss: 6941-8, 6950-7, 6960-4, 6559, 6598].

Public Record Office, Kew (names listed without location in the county)

Militia: **Monmouthshire and Brecon: 1780-1876** [WO.13/1510-35]; **Brecon: 1820-76** [WO.13/170-77].
Local Militia: **East, West: 1808-16** [WO.13/3414-5].
Note. No Supplementary Militia regiment listed; probably with Monmouthshire.

CAERNARVONSHIRE

Caernarfon Area Record Office (Gwynedd Archives Service), Caernarfon.

Militia Ballot Lists
1812. Pwllheli sub-div. [Lieutenancy].

Public Record Office, Kew.

County Regimental Returns (names listed without location in the county)
Militia: **1781-1876** [WO.13/284-307].
Supplementary Militia: **1798-1814** [WO.13/2482].
Local Militia: **1808-16** [WO.13/3428].

CARDIGANSHIRE

Ceredigion Record Office, Aberystwyth.

Militia Enrolment Book
1827. Royal Cardigan Militia: **County,** by parish (250 names) [no ref.]. Modern name index.

Public Record Office, Kew.

County Regimental Returns (names listed without location in the county)
Militia: **1780-1876** [WO.13/233-57].
Supplementary Militia: **1798-1814** [WO.13/2480].
Local Militia: **1808-16** [WO.13/3423].

CARMARTHENSHIRE

Note. There are no relevant records at Carmarthen County Record Office.

Public Record Office, Kew.

County Regimental Returns (names listed without location in the county)
Militia: **1780-1876** [WO.13/258-83].
Supplementary Militia: **1800-16** [WO.13/2481].
Local Militia: **1st, 2nd, 3rd: 1808-16** [WO.13/3425-7].

DENBIGHSHIRE

Publications
Yeomanry Cavalry: **1820-22** (250) [P.R.O.
WO.13/3982] in 'Pay Lists and returns for
the Denbighshire Yeomanry Cavalry in
Assemblies at Wrexham, 1820, and Ruthin,
1822', W. Alister Williams, *Hel Achau*
(Journal of Clwyd F.H.S.) **10** (Summer
1983). Also contains lists of officers: 1825,
1839, 1853, 1860, 1871.

Clwyd Record Office, Ruthin.

Militia Ballot List
*c.*1800. Park township (par. Henllan) (10)
[Denbigh Borough Records BD/A/66].

Volunteers
1860-69. Drill roll, Denbighshire Volunteers
[DD/DM/369/1].

The National Library of Wales, Aberystwyth.

Levee en Masse List
1803. Llangernyw (men, 17-55) [Wigfair
2769].

Public Record Office, Kew.

County Regimental Returns (names listed
without location in the county)
Militia: **1780-1876** [WO.13/422-46].
Supplementary Militia: **1798-1816**
[WO.13/2487].
Local Militia: **Central, East, West: 1808-16**
[WO.13/3446-8].

FLINTSHIRE

Clwyd Record Office, Hawarden.

Yeomanry Muster Rolls
1798. Wrexham Yeomanry [D/E/3132].
*c.*1831-3. Hawarden, Mold, Border Troops
of Flints. Yeomanry Cavalry [D/HA/1261-5,
1273-83 *passim*].
1831-38. Members of Flints. Yeomanry
Cavalry [D/DM/256/2].

Militia Muster Rolls
1803-13. Rhuddlan and Prestatyn sub-divs.
Flintshire Militia [D/DM/16].

Public Record Office, Kew.

County Regimental Returns (names listed
without location in the county)
Militia: **1780-1876** [WO.13/755-77].
Supplementary Militia: **1801-15**
[WO.13/2501].
Local Militia: **Flint; 1st, 2nd, 3rd: 1808-16**
[WO.13/3483-6].

GLAMORGAN

Glamorgan Record Office, Cardiff.

Militia Ballot Lists
1763. Neath Hd. [D/D Xei 11/1-20;
photocopy from original in private hands].
1828. Upper Caerphilly sub-div. (1,774)
[LCM 2].

Public Record Office, Kew.

County Regimental Returns (names listed
without location in the county)
Militia: **Glamorgan: 1780-1876**
[WO.13/805-29]; **Glamorgan Artillery:
1854-76** [WO.13/830-33].
Supplementary Militia: **1800-16**
[WO.13/2503].
Local Militia: **Centre, Eastern, Western:
1808-16** [WO.13/3490-2].

MERIONETH

Publications
Militia Ballot List: **1827.** Ffestiniog (206
names) [University College of North Wales
Bangor Mss 1485], in 'The Militia List of
the parish of Ffestioniog, Mer., 1827', by
John Buckley, *Gwreiddiau or Gwynedd
Roots* **11** (Gwynedd F.H.S.) (Nov. 1986),
pp.14-15.
*Merioneth Volunteers and Local Militia durir
the Napoleonic Wars (1795-1816),* by
Hugh J. Owen (Dolgellau, 1934).

Clwyd Record Office, Hawarden.

Militia Muster Roll
1788. Penllyn Hd. [D/NH/1114].

*Department of Manuscripts, University
College of North Wales Library, Bangor.*

Militia Ballot List
1827. Ffestiniog (206) [Bangor Mss. 1485
Published.

Note. There are no relevant records at the
Dolgellau Area Record Office, Gwynedd
Archives Service.

Public Record Office, Kew.

County Regimental Returns (names listed
without location in the county)
Militia: **1796-1876** [WO.13/1396-1418].
Supplementary Militia: **1799-1814** [2527].
Local Militia: **1808-16** [WO.13/3553].

MONMOUTHSHIRE
(administratively in England until 1974)

National Library of Wales, Aberystwyth.

Militia Muster Rolls [Tredegar Park]
1759. Wentloog **Hd.** [59/17]; **Hds.** of **Usk,**
Caldicott [113/17,18]; **Hds.** of **Ragland,**
Abergavenny [113/25,26].
1766. Caldicott **Hd.** [113/19,20].

Gwent County Record Office, Cwmbran.

Muster Book
1809-12. Loyal Monmouthshire Volunteer
Cavalry (70 per muster).

Militia Ballot Lists
1826. 34 parishes and townships in **Hds.** of
Raglan, Skenfrith and **Usk,** with
Monmouth Borough (1,677) [Lieutenancy
records].
1831. 13 parishes in **Caldicot Hd.** (1,040)
[private solicitor's collection].

Militia Enrolment List
1852, 1853. Royal Monmouthshire Militia
(listed by hd.) (600).

Public Record Office, Kew.

County Regimental Returns (names listed
without location in the county)
Militia: **Monmouths. and Brecon:**
1780-1876 [WO.13/1510-35].
Supplementary Militia: **Monmouths.:**
1798-1815 [WO.13/2533].
Local Militia: **East, West: 1808-16**
[WO.13/3557-8].

MONTGOMERYSHIRE

Note. No relevant material is held by the
National Library of Wales.

Public Record Office, Kew.

County Regimental Returns (names listed
without location in the county)
Militia: **1780-1876** [WO.13/1536-59].
Supplementary Militia: **1798-1814**
[WO.13/2534].
Local Militia: **East, West: 1808-16**
[WO.13/3559-60].

PEMBROKESHIRE

Note. No relevant material is held by the
Pembrokeshire Record Office..

Public Record Office, Kew.

County Regimental Returns (names listed
without location in the county)
Militia: **1780-1876** [WO.13.1729-52].
Supplementary Militia: **1798-1813**
[WO.13/2541].
Local Militia: **Pembroke, Pembroke South:**
1808-16 [WO.13/3583-4].

RADNORSHIRE

The National Library of Wales, Aberystwyth.

Militia Ballot Lists
1775. St. Harmon, Nanmel, Llansantffraid
Cwmdeuddwr and Llan-llyr [Misc. Coll. II,
nos. 32, 34-37].

Public Record Office, Kew.

County Regimental Returns (names listed
without location in the county)
Militia: **1781-1876** [WO.13/1776-99].
Supplementary Militia: **1799-1814**
[WO.13/2543].
Local Militia: **1808-16** [WO.13/3589].

SCOTLAND

Records of musters up to the Act of Union of 1707 are at the **Scottish Record Office** in Edinburgh, scattered through a variety of collections of family papers. The Militia was only re-established in Scotland at the very end of the 18th century, but there were many less official bands of volunteer soldiers, particularly of course in 1745-46.

The holdings of the Scottish Record Office for the period up to the Act of Union in 1707 are listed in *Tudor and Stuart Muster Rolls*. Those post-1707 to the later eighteenth century, and those from the later eighteenth century on, are listed here. A few relate to the Regular Army, and, as it has been necessary to rely on the catalogue entries rather than any physical examination, some may not in fact include nominal rolls of any sort. Further information will be welcome. Apart from the chronological grouping, the entries are left in the order of the individual family collections with no attempt at geographical arrangement.

Regimental returns for the re-established Militia from 1798 on are at the Public Record Office at Kew, but these are unlikely to provide details of whence within the regiment's catchment area recruits may have come.

Publications

Muster Roll of Prince Charles Edward Stuart's Army 1745-6, edited by C.W.H. Livingstone, C.W.H. Aikman and B.S. Hart (1984). Lists by Regiments about 5,900 names (some with age), occupation, residence and fate after battle.

Muster Roll for the Forfar or Lord Ogilvy's Regiment, raised on behalf of the Royal House of Stuart, 1745-6, by Alexander Mackintosh (Inverness, 1914). Lists alphabetically, as to rank, name, occupation, residence, parish, county and fate after battle. About 550 names with 65 biographical sketches of same.

'The Edinburgh County Militia of 1799', David Dobson, *The Scottish Genealogist*, 31, 3, pp.90-91; based on contemporary newspapers (see *Directory of Scottish Newspapers*, Joan P. Ferguson, National Library of Scotland, 1984).

For popular reaction to the Militia Act see *Popular Disturbances in Scotland, 1780-1815* (Chapter 3), by Kenneth J. Logue (John Donald Publishers, Edinburgh, 1979), and the intellectual debate over militia forces is described in *The Scottish Enlightenment and the Militia Issue*, by John Robertson (John Donald, 1985).

Scottish Record Office, Edinburgh.

Eighteenth century, 1707 – 1770's

Leven and Melville papers
1707-8. Muster rolls of troops in North Britain [GD.26/9/391].

1708. Lists of the Artillery company in Scotland [GD.26/9/422].

1712. 'A list of the men discharged in August'; 'A list of the squades' [GD.26/9/466-7].

c.1750. Detailed list of men in Lord Balgonie's company [GD.26/9/499].

Robertson of Kindeace papers
c.1713-97. Muster rolls, *etc.* [GD.146/Box 18/1-3].

1714. Militia raised in Duddington parish [GD.331/18].

Sandilands of Eastbarn papers
1715. Capt. George Sandeland's company [GD.1/382/36].

Hume of Polwarth papers
1715. Muster of heritors in parish of Lawder [GD.158/402].

1715. Men sent from Dirleton to keep guard at Seton [GD.6/1092]. Fencible men and militia foot soldiers in the parish of Dirleton [GD.6/1094-5].

Clerk of Pencuik muniments
1715. Prisoners taken at Preston [GD.18/3158].

1733. Roll of height and age of men in King's troop [GD.6/1098].

1745. Sutherland Fencibles [GD.1/400/4/2].

1745. Mustering of volunteers, Holyrood [GD.331/18].

Cardross writs
1746. Muster rolls of companies in Brig. Gen. John Price's regt. of Foot, Fort Augustus [GD.15/893/1/1-9].
1746. Muster rolls of companies in the King's regt. of Foot commanded by Lieut. Gen. Barrell, Fort Augustus [GD.15/893/2/1-5].
1746. Muster roll of Capt. William Cunningham's company, 2nd battalion, Royal regt. of Foot, commanded by Lieut. Gen. James St. Clair, Inverness [GD.15/893/3].
1746. Muster roll of Capt. John Romer's company, King's regt. of Foot, commanded by Lt. Gen. Barrell [GD.15/894].

Rose of Kilravock muniments
?1746. Sick men in Lord John Murray's Highlanders and other regts. [GD.125/23/13/5].
1761. Muster rolls of Capt. William Rose's company, Sutherland Highlanders [GD.125/Box 24/1].

Craigmillar charters
1750. Pay sheets of Capt. Little's company of Militia [GD.122/842-3].

Ross Estate muniments
1762. Meeting of **Dumbartonshire** heritors and freeholders to apply for establishment of a militia [GD.47/371].

Campbell of Balliveolan papers
1778. Attestation with personal details of volunteers, Argyllshire Highland regt. of Foot [GD.13/90].

Campbell of Barcaldine papers
1775-6. Recruits for Maj. Gen. Simon Fraser's 71st regt. [GD.170/3435].
1778. Roll of Capt. James Campbell's recruits [GD.170/3447-8].

Elphinstone muniments
1668-1807. Militia papers [GD.156/Box 56/4].

Late Eighteenth Century and Nineteenth Century

Breadalbane muniments
1775-1860. Papers on Breadalbane Fencibles, incl. muster rolls, recruiting lists, American Service rolls [GD.112/52/1-70].

Gordon Castle muniments
1776-1817. Papers of the Northern Fencibles [GD.44/47/1-25].
1794-1811. Papers of militia, Militia Club, Volunteers in **Aberdeenshire** [GD.44/47/26-47, GD.44/50/3].

Buccleuch muniments
1788-1879. Many militia papers, mostly relating to **Edinburgh**: South Fencible regt.; Edinburgh regt. of Militia; Edinburgh County Militia; Dumfriesshire Militia [GD.224/423-51].
1794-1800. Papers on 1st Fencible Light Dragoons [GD.224/687/1].
1797-98. Papers on Musselburgh Volunteers [GD.224/687/2].

Fraser Mackintosh collection
1780-85. Papers of 71st regt. [GD.128/53/6].
1797-1807. Papers of **Inverness-shire** Volunteers [GD.128/47/1-3].

Seafield papers
n.d. Lists of enrolments *etc.*, regarding 1st Fencible regt. of Highlanders, and **Inverness and Strathspey** Militia and Volunteers [GD.248.213/5-7].
1793-98. Muster rolls of 1st regt. of Fencible Highlanders [GD.248/2014-5].
1794-96. Muster roll, 97th regt. of Foot [GD.248/2032].

1794. Muster roll of the Cameron Highlanders [GD.1/400/4/4].

Maclaine of Lochbuie papers
1790's. Men on Lochbuy estate who are fit and unfit for military service [GD.174/922-24, 927].
?1794. Men liable for militia ballot, Torosay [GD.174/2231].
1820. Volunteers for a company to be raised at Ballimeanich [GD.174/2316].

1795. Muster roll of the Reay Fencibles [GD.1/400/4/4].

Airlie muniments
1797-99. Breadalbane Fencibles, 1st battalion, monthly pay lists and muster rolls [GD.16/52/25].
1847. Dundee Enrolled Force [GD.16/52/52].
19th cent. Names of Panmure tenants likely to join Panmure troop of Yeomanry [GD.16/52-59].
n.d. Airlie troop [GD.16/53/39].

Seaforth muniments
1797-1800. Papers on Highland militia, particularly 2nd regt. of North British Militia [GD.46/6/36-69].
1799-1865. Papers on volunteers and local militia, particularly 1st Ross-shire local militia [GD.46/6/56, 59, 70-83a].
1808-16. Wigtownshire militia papers [GD.46/6/3-21].

Papers of East Lothian Antiquarian and Field Naturalists Society
1797-1838. Muster rolls relating to volunteers, militia and yeomanry [GD.302/1 (27 items)].
1799-1813. Papers relating to **Dunbar** Volunteer Infantry [WD.302/29 (27 items)].
1803-09. Papers relating to **East Lothian** Yeomanry [GD.302/44 (52 items)].

Dalguise muniments
1798. Subscription by cottars and tenants of Dalguise towards national defence [GD.38/1/1156].
1817. Regimental lists with the names of 'my regiment' [GD.38/1/1206].
1827. Roll of the Grenadier company, 42nd regt. [GD/38/1/1225].

Murton papers
1798-1807. Muster rolls of **Midlothian** Yeomanry Cavalry [GD.150/2364].
n.d. 'Arbuthnot's' troop' quartered at Corstorphine [GD.150/2938].

Messrs. Todd, Murray and Jamieson, W.S., collection
c.1798. Renfrewshire: detailed return of men between 15 and 60, weapons, *etc.*, [GD.237/192/3].

Dundas of Ochertyre muniments
1799-1803. Kincardine militia papers [GD.35/260].

Peebles Lieutenancy
1799-1800, 1803, 1806. Peebles Militia, muster rolls [GD.293/3/15-17].
1808-11. Same [GD.293/19-21, 23].
1812-14. Peebles Militia, volunteers enrolled [GD.293/3/24].
1813. Peebles Militia, balloting papers [GD.293/3/25-26].
1813, 1819-22. Peebles Militia, muster rolls [GD.293/3/27-29].
1820-22, 1825-31. Peebles Militia, muster rolls [GD.293/3/30-34].

Sutherland of Forse muniments
1790's-1815. Papers on **Caithness** militia [GD.139/267/1-8].

Sinclair of Freswick papers
c.1800. Papers of Freswick and Dunbeath Volunteers [GD.136/1211-29].
1804-06. Petitions on ballotting for army of reserve, **Caithness** [GD.136/1220].

Campbell of Balliveolan papers
1801. Letter with return of recruits, Reay Fencibles [GD.13/308].

Robertson of Lude muniments
1801. Return of Atholl Volunteers [GD.132/833].
1807-10. Papers of Clandonachy Volunteers [GD.132/793].

Messrs. Bruce and Kerr, W.S., collection
1809-12. Buteshire regt. of Local Militia, pay list [GD.240/Box 20/1].

1812. Return of houses, families and persons (incl. French prisoners of war) in parish of **Jedburgh** [GD.2/397].

Balfour-Melville papers
1820-38. Muster books, Royal **Fifeshire** Yeomanry Cavalry [GD.126/Box 26].

Dalhousie muniments
1822. Return of men, women and children in military settlements of Perth, Richmond and Lanark [GD.45/3/363].
1827. Nominal returns of Quebec Light Cavalry, Quebec Volunteer Rifle company and Quebec Artillery [GD.45/3/398].

Cromartie muniments
1826-7. Militia (ballot) lists for the parish of Lochbroom [GD.305/557].

Scottish Record Office continued

Kirkness papers from Marshall Museum, Kinross
n.d. Men to be ballotted for militia, parish of Portmoak [GD.1/49/164].
n.d. Petitions for exclusion from **Fife** militia ballot [GD.1/49/166-7].

Hamilton Bruce papers
1838. Members of Stratheden troop of Yeomanry [GD.152/83].

Public Record Office, Kew (all in Class WO.13/).

County, etc., Regimental Returns (names listed without location in the county)
(*M* = Militia: all **1798-1876** unless shown otherwise; *SM* = Supplementary Militia; *LM* = Local Militia: all **1808-16**).

Aberdeen: *M* [1-25]; *SM:* **1802-16** [2471]; *LM:* **1st-5th** [3394-8].
Argyll and Bute: *M* [51-72]; *SM* (Argyll only): **1804-14** [2473]; *LM* (Argyll only): **1st-3rd** [3400-2].
Ayrshire: *M* [73-98]; *SM:* **1805-16** [2474]; *LM:* **1st-3rd, Rifles** [3403-6].
Banff: *LM* [3407].
Berwickshire: *M:* **1803-59** [154-69]; *SM:* **1802-15** [2478]; *LM* [3413].
Bute: *LM* [3419]. See also under Argyll.
Caithness: *LM* [3420].
Clackmannan and Kinross: *LM* [3433].
Dumbarton: *LM* [3464].
Dumfries: *M* [585-607]; *SM:* **1805-14** [2494]; *LM:* **1st, Annandale and Eskdale, Nithsdale** [3465-7].
East Lothian – see Haddington.
Edinburgh: *M:* [644-67]; *Artillery:* **1854-76** [668-72]; *SM:* **1798-1815** [2496]; *LM:* **1st (Highland), 2nd, 3rd** [3470-2]. See also Midlothian.
Elgin: *LM* [3473].
Fife: *M* [731-54]; *SM:* **1800-16** [2500]; *LM:* **1st-3rd, Queensferry** [3479-82].

P.R.O., Kew continued

Forfar and Kincardine: *M* [778-803]; *SM* (Forfar only): **1801-16** [2502]; *LM* (Forfar only): **Centre, Eastern, Western** [3487-9]. See also Kincardine.
Galloway: *M:* **1852-59** [804].
Haddington: *M:* **1860-76** [888-90]; *LM* [3497].
Highland Rifles: *M:* *1867-76* [1012-13]. See also Ross.
Highland Light Infantry: *M:* **1872-76** [1014].
Highland Borderers: *M:* *1872-76* [1015]. See also Stirling.
Inverness: *M:* **1803-76** [1039-54]; *SM:* **1802-14** [2512]; *LM:* **1st-4th** [3508-11].
Kincardine: *LM* [3519]. See also Forfar.
Kinross: *LM* [3520].
Kirkcudbright: *M:* **1803-51** [1114-26]; *SM:* **1805-15** [2515]; *LM* [3521].
Lanarkshire: *M* [1127-50]; **2nd Lanarkshire: 1855-76** [1151-57]; *SM:* **1802-14** [2516]; *LM:* **1st-6th** [3522-7].
Linlithgow: *LM* [3552].
Lothian, East – see Haddington.
Lothian, West – see Linlithgow.
Midlothian: *LM:* **1st-3rd** [3554-6]. See also Edinburgh.
Nairn: *LM* [3561].
Perth: *M* [1753-75]; *SM:* **1802-16** [2542]; *LM:* **Central, East, Highland, West** [3585-8].
Renfrew: *M:* **1803-76** [1800-20]; *SM:* **1803-15** [2544]; *LM:* **1st-3rd** [3590-2].
Ross (North British): *M:* **1798-1867** [1821-41] (after 1867 called Highland Rifles); *SM:* **1801-16** [2545]; *LM:* **East, West** [3593-4].
Roxburgh: *LM:* **1st, 2nd** [3595-6].
Scottish Borderers: see Dumfries.
Stirling: *M:* **1803-72** [1990-2008] (1872-76: see Highland Borderers); *SM:* **1803-14** [2555]; *LM:* **East, West** [3615-6].
Sutherland: *LM* [3629].
West Lothian – see Linlithgow.
Wigtown: *LM* [3637].

CHANNEL ISLANDS

La Societe Jersiaise, 9 Pier Road, St. Helier, Jersey.

Note. The collection is only partially catalogued, and where documents are undated only very approximate dating can be suggested. Pre-19th century documents are all ref. E.7/M.9.

Muster Lists
1722, 1724, 1729. Capt. Charles de Carteret's company (20 each).
n.d. (18th cent.). South regt. (1st, 2nd, 3rd, 4th companies, and artillery) (40 each).
n.d. (18th cent.). Fusilier company, Trinity regt.
1806, 1815. General Don's muster lists (and census summary of all parishes) (500) [E.8].
1809-37. St. Laurens (Lawrence) battn. and 3rd or East regt, some lists from orderly books.
1815. Muster list, 1st or North West regt., arranged by districts [E.7/M.4].
Note. The Genealogical Section includes a register of baptisms, marriages and burials of troops in garrison in Jersey, **1784-1817.**

Priaulx Library, Candie Road, St. Peter Port, Guernsey.

18th-19th cents.: Royal Guernsey Militia records. These do *not* include any muster lists.

Public Record Office, Kew.

Regimental Returns (names listed without location)
Guernsey: 1843-52 [WO.13/887].
Jersey: 1843-52 [WO.13/1055].

ISLE OF MAN

Manx Museum Library, Douglas.

Manx Fencibles
MS and printed records of the regt., incl. enlistment books (showing rank, age, height, colour of eyes, complexion, place of birth and date of enlistment) [Mss MD.40/10 and 11; see also index to printed matter, Military, Manx Fencibles, B.114].

IRELAND

Public Record Office, *Dublin.*
ex. *Handbook on Irish Genealogy* (Heraldic Artists, 1973), p.41)

791-1860. Longford Militia [M.3474-3483]. 10 vols.
855-57. Sligo Militia [M.2558-63]. 7 vols.

Genealogical Office, *Dublin.*
ex. *Handbook on Irish Genealogy,* p.45)

Militia Lists
761: Counties Limerick, Cork, Tipperary, Kerry, Derry, Louth, Wicklow, Monaghan, Roscommon, Down, Donegal, Dublin, Tyrone [M.579].

Public Record Office, *Belfast.*
ex. *Handbook on Irish Genealogy,* p.44)

indlay and Williams Collection: military records, consisting of militia and army lists.

Public Record Office, *Kew* (all in Class WO.13/).

County etc. Regimental Returns (names listed without location in the county)

Antrim: 1793-1876 [2574-96]; **Artillery: 1854-76** [2597-602].
Armagh: 1793-1876 [2603-24]; **Artillery: 1855-67** [2625-26].
Carlow: 1793-1876 [2627-46].
Cavan: 1794-1876 [2647-66].
Clare: 1793-1876 [2667-86].
Cork City: 1793-1876 [2687-705].
Cork (North): 1793-1876 [2706-26]; **Cork (South): 1793-1876** [2727-46]; **Cork (West) Artillery: 1855-76** [2747-50].

P.R.O., Kew continued

Donegal: 1793-1876 [2751-71]; **Artillery: 1855-76** [2772-75].
Down, North: 1793-1876 [2776-96]; **South: 1800-76** [2797-814].
Dublin City: 1793-1876 [2815-35]; **Artillery: 1855-76** [2836-40].
Dublin County: 1793-1876 [2841-60].
Fermanagh: i**793-1876** [2861-81].
Galway: 1793-1876 [2882-901].
Kerry: 1793-1876 [2902-22].
Kildare: 1793-1876 [2923-41].
Kilkenny: 1793-1876 [2942-60].
King's County: 1793-1876 [2961-79].
Leitrim: 1793-1876 [2980-98].
Limerick City: 1793-1876 [2999-3017].
Limerick County: 1783-1876 [3018-38].
Londonderry: 1793-1876 [3039-58].
Longford: 1793-1876 [3059-78].
Louth: 1793-1876 [3079-100].
Mayo (North): 1793-1876 [3101-20]; **(South): 1793-1876** [3121-40].
Meath: 1793-1876 [3141-59].
Monaghan: 1793-1876 [3160-79].
Queen's County: 1793-1876 [3180-98].
Roscommon: 1793-1876 [3199-219].
Sligo: 1793-1876 [3220-37].
Tipperary, 1st (South): 1854-76 [3238-42]; **2nd (North): 1793-1876** [3243-63].
Tyrone: 1793-1876 [3264-83]; **Artillery: 1855-76** [3284-87].
Waterford: 1793-1876 [3288-309].
Westmeath: 1793-1876 [3310-29].
Wexford: 1793-1876 [3330-50].
Wicklow: 1793-1876 [3351-70].

1st-6th Light Battalions (Ireland): 1803-1806 [3371-93].